A TEXT BOOK OF ENVIRONMENTAL SCIENCE

In accordance with the latest syllabus prescribed by the Council for the Indian School CertificateExaminations, New Delhi.

A TEXT BOOK OF ENVIRONMENTAL SCIENCE

CLASS X

Manasa Sampat Hegde
M. Sc., Chemistry
PGDESD

OSWAL PUBLISHERS
1/12 Sahitya Kunj, M. G. Road, Agra-282 002

Edition : 2021

ISBN : 978-93-88623-09-4

OSWAL PUBLISHERS

Head office : 1/12, Sahitya Kunj, M. G. Road, Agra-282 002
Phone : (0562) 2527771-4, +91 75340 77222
E-mail : contact@oswalpublishers.com
Website : www.oswalpublishers.com
Printed at

Preface

In order to meet the economic, cultural, social and aesthetic needs of people all over the globe, a holistic understanding of our environmental Education equips learners with the knowledge, essential. Environmental skills, and motivation to address complex environmental challenges in the 21st Century. Oswal's 'A Text book of Environmental Studies' brings to you the relation between economy, environment and social community and introduces the concept of Sustainable Development. It also familiarizes learners with various strategies towards sustainable development. The limitations and benefits of these strategies are also detailed in the chapters. Through the activities and exercises that are provided in this book, learners and teachers are encouraged to explore on the topics of Environmental Conservation and Sustainable Development.

The chapters and exercises are written in accordance to the syllabus prescribed by ICSE. Some significant latest advancements in the field of environmental science and sustainable development have also been incorporated in the form of examples and facts. There are 10 chapters in this book and each has been composed and assembled in a way that helps the learners to understand the inter-connection between the concepts.

We hope this book will enable the readers to strengthen their understanding of the Concepts of Environmental Science.

All suggestions regarding the book are welcome.

The Publishers

SYLLABUS CLASS X

ENVIRONMENT

There will be one paper of two hours duration carrying 80 marks and Internal Assessment of 20 marks.

The paper will have ***two*** *Sections :*

Section A *(Compulsory) will contain short answer questions covering the entire syllabus.*

Section B *will contain* ***six*** *questions. Candidates will be required to answer any* ***four*** *questions from this section.*

1. Controlling Air Pollution

(a) From domestic combustion.

Reducing pollution from domestic cooking; clean cooking – kerosene as a desirable cooking fuel in rural areas.

(b) From industries.

Measures for controlling industrial air pollution – technological measures (energy efficient devices, clean technologies), meteorological controls; zoning strategy; penalties and subsidies, Case Study : the Taj Trapezium.

(c) From vehicles.

Vehicle emission control – modify engine design (catalytic converters, four stroke engines), clean fuels, public transport options, traffic management, economic policy measures.

2. Addressing Population

(a) The link between growing population and environmental degradation.

UN's population projections for 2050, the climate link, the choice of alternative futures. Growing population in the developing countries and rising consumption in the developed countries.

(b) The demographic transition.

Stages of transition, transition stages of certain developed nations and developing nations (such as India, China, Korea, Malaysia). ***Not to be tested, for knowledge and understanding only.***

(c) Strategies for controlling growth of population.

Strategies to includejamily planning and birth control, health care, education, economic development; women-centered human development.

(d) Development framework for poverty alleviation.

Social mobilisation, agricultural development, small-scale industries, human development. ***Not to be tested, for knowledge and understanding only.***

3. Managing the Urban environment

(a) Urbanisation – a challenge to the future.

Sustainable cities : the need of the hour.

(b) Planning environmental improvement.

Effcient land use, planning energy, shelter and transport; water supply management, waste water and sanitary waste management, construction activities.

(c) Rural development to counter migration.

Self-explanatory.

(d) Development of secondary cities to counter migration.

Self-explanatory.

(e) Community participation and contribution of private enterprises.

Community participation in keeping surroundings clean, participation of private enterprises in city improvement, measures to increase private enterprise participation.

4. Managing Soil and Land

(a) Conserving soil.

Erosion control techniques – terracing, contour ploughing, dry farming, tree planting, bunds, gullies, wind-breaks, use of organic fertilizers.

Soil conservation techniques – land-use management, vegetative and mechanical practices, conserving soil and water together; appropriate cropping systems – cropping patterns (strip cropping), tree crops, and foliage crops.

(b) Land reforms.

Meaning, measures enforced in India to give land to the landless.

(c) Integrated rural development.

Objectives, self-help schemes like social and community forestry.

(d) Role of women and community in conservation.

Self-explanatory.

(e) Combating deforestation.

Reforestation, energy plantations, forest harvesting of non-timber forest products, exploring alternative sources of livelihood, change in consumption patterns.

(f) Managing forest grazing.

Causes and consequences of overgrazing, controlled forest grazing as in National Forest Policy, 1988.

(g) Alternatives to timber.

Recycling of timber and paper.

5. Food

(a) Sustainable agriculture.

Integrated pest management – understanding the term, aims, advantages, disadvantages.

Genetically modified organisms, application in plants and animals and environmental risks.

New crop strains – high yielding varieties and their viability, hybrid varieties.

Mixed cropping – advantages and disadvantages; regenerative farming techniques – intercropping, crop rotation, agro forestiy, polyvarietal cultivation and polyculture.

Conservation tillage farming - meaning of conservation tillage, advantages and disadvantages.

Trickle drip irrigation – need for a trickle drip irrigation system; operation of a drip irrigation system; advantages and disadvantages.

New organic fertilizers – integrated nutrient supply programme, organic fertilizers - bulky organic manures, green manures, bio-fertilizers, and sewage sludge.

Gene banks — what are gene banks; objectives of maintaining gene banks.

(b) Problem of global food security, food aid.

Global food imbalance, distributional inequality; role of food aid in achieving global food security.

6. Biodiversity

(a) Biodiversity at risk due to human actions.

Reasons for loss of biodiversity; Man - the super consumer : impact of his actions on the earth's resources; reasons for concern : economic, ecological and aesthetic.

(b) Conserving our genetic resource: in-situ and ex-situ; harvesting wildlife.

In-situ – wildlife sanctuaries, national parks and biosphere reserves.

Ex-situ – zoological parks, botanical gardens, gene banks in agricultural research centres and forestry institutions.

Harvesting wildlife to meet commercial needs.

(c) Conservation strategies at national and international levels.

Wildlife (Protection) Act 1972, Project Tiger 1973, IUCN, the Ramsar Convention on Wetlands, 1971, CITES, The Convention on Biological Diversity.

7. Energy

(a) Fossil fuels used to produce electricity.

Electricity : energy on demand; dwindling supplies of fossil fuels; renewable and non-renewable energy resources. ***Not to be tested, for knowledge and understanding only.***

(b) Nuclear energy.

Nuclear fission, advantages and disadvantages of nuclear energy; safety concerns (the Chernobyl disaster); nuclear fusion.

(c) A sustainable energy future.

Energy conservation; alternative energy sources – solar energy, wind energy, hydroelectricity, geothermal energy, biomass, liquid fuels from biomass- methanol, ethanol, gasohol, CNG, hydrogen.

8. Waste

(a) Solid waste : the throwaway society.

Solid waste, biodegradable and non-biodegradable materials; where does the trash go - landfills and incinerators.

(b) Solid waste : options for the future.

Producing less waste, reusing, recycling, composting, vermiculture, biotechnology; finding alternatives to materials we use.

9. Environment and Development

(a) Global environmental pollution.

Who is responsible - developed or developing countries? Need for mutual cooperation.

(b) Economic development and environmental degradation.

Role of developed and developing countries; contrasting views of developed and developing countries; debt trap.

(c) International trade.

Its link to environmental deterioration – unfair trade practices.

(d) Role of multinational corporations.

Definition of MNCs, their contribution to development and debatable contribution to environment; case study – Bhopal gas tragedy; measures to regulate activities of MNCs in developing countries.

10. Towards a Sustainable Future

(a) Global interdependence – economic and environmental.

Concept of economic and environmental global interdependence; global environmental health – the shared responsibility of nations; trade and aid as ways of reducing world inequalities.

(b) International cooperation.

The Montreal Protocol; the Global Environmental Facility (GEF) support; the Earth Summit, UN 's International Conference on Population and Development (Cairo); the Kyoto Treaty.

(c) Sustainable development.

The concept of sustainable development, sustainable development and developed countries; sustainable development and developing countries.

(d) Role of non-governmental organisations.

Self-explanatory.

(e) Technology that sustains.

Satellite imagery as a means of monitoring the global environment: satellite remote sensing, advantages in collecting environmental data, applying data in areas of environmental damage as deforestation, desertification, land degradation, wastelands, mining, ozone layer depletion and predicting droughts and foods.

The concept of alternate technology, adopting alternate technology to create self-sustaining societies in the developed and developing world.

Role of biotechnology in achieving global food security.

INTERNAL ASSESSMENT

A minimum of three assignments as prescribed by the teacher, need to be completed.

Suggested Assignments

1. Make a field study of the effect of human interaction on the natural environment and write a project report (1500 words) on the likely impact of the interaction on the global environment.
2. Prepare an original study/essay (2000 words) on an area of the prescribed curriculum that is indicative of his/her appreciation/ concern for environmental issues and make a functional model to support the above.

EVALUATION

The assignments/project work are to be evaluated by the subject teacher and by an External Examiner.

(The External Examiner may be a teacher nominated by the Head of the school, who could be from the faculty, but not teaching the subject in the section/class. For example, a teacher of EVS of Class Vlll may be deputed to be an External Examiner for Class X, Environmental Science projects.)

The Internal Examiner and the External Examiner will assess the assignments independently.

Award of marks (20 Marks)

Subject Teacher (lnternal Examiner) 10 marks

External Examiner 10 marks

The total marks obtained out of 20 are to be sent to the Council by the Head of the school.

The Head ofthe school will be responsible for the entry of marks on the mark sheets provided by the Council.

CONTENTS

1 CONTROLLING AIR POLLUTION

1.0 INTRODUCTION

Pollution is caused when contaminants are induced into the natural environment that causes adverse changes. **Pollution** is thus defined as the effect of undesirable change in our surroundings that have harmful effects on plants, animals and human beings. Substances which cause pollution are called as **pollutants**. Human activities like urbanisation, industrialisation and other advancements in technologies has reaped us immense economic gain along with an easy and comfortable lifestyle. But, we have contaminated and polluted our air, water and land on which life exists to gain these benefits.

Pollution can take the form of chemical substances or energy, such as noise, heat or light. Its unpleasant effects are damaging for the healthy survival and also the contamination in most cass is not completely reversible. Pollution is drastically rising in all the countries due to rise in human activity associated with modern technology and population growth. Even the daily normal livelihood requirements are high contributing factors to never ending pollution of all sorts. Thus, pollution control is the responsibility of every citizen around the globe.

1.1 AIR POLLUTION

Air pollution is the addition of harmful substances in air that degrades the air quality, causing severe damage to the environment and the health of living beings. Air quality is defined as the degree to which the air in a particular place is pollution-free. Air pollution is not a recent phenomenon, its origin can be traced back to the times when man first started using firewood for his daily chores. However, it became more noticeable by the beginning of 20th century with advancement of urbanisation, transportation and industrialisation. Major pollutants of air are carbon monoxide, carbon dioxide, sulphur dioxide, methane, chlorofluorocarbons and particulate dust.

Main sources of the air pollution are :

(i) Domestic combustion

(ii) Industrial waste

(iii) Vehicular emission

1.2 CONTROLLING AIR POLLUTION

Air pollution causes damage to crops, animals, forests and water bodies. It also contributes to the depletion of the ozone layer, which protects the Earth from the sun's UV rays. Another negative effect of air pollution is the formation of acid rain, which harms trees, soils, rivers and wildlife. It also causes long term and short-term health issues in human beings. Pollution prevention protects the environment by conserving and protecting natural resources while strengthening economic growth through more efficient production in industry and less need for households, businesses and communities to handle waste.

Fascinating Fact

45% of the population of Copenhagen commute by bicycle to their work or study places every day.

(i) From Domestic Combustion

Combustion or burning is a chemical reaction where fuel burns in presence of oxygen to produce energy.

Fuel + oxygen → Carbon dioxide + water

Combustion of fuel is incomplete if there is inadequate oxygen which produces by- products like carbon monoxide, polynuclear aromatic hydrocarbons (PAHs), oxides of sulphur and nitrogen and particulates. These substances are potential pollutants which considerably reduce the air quality and cause harm to life in that vicinity. These gases are poisonous and contribute to global warming and acid rain too. Our daily use appliances include gas ranges, furnaces, gas water heaters, gas clothes dryers, wood or coal-burning stoves and fireplaces which use fuels like CNG, LPG, fuel oil, kerosene, wood or coal. The types and amounts of pollutants produced depend upon the type of appliance, how well the appliance is installed, maintained, and vented, and the kind of fuel it uses.

Fascinating Fact

Approximately 92% of the world's population lives in places where air pollution exceeds safe limits.

Pollution caused due to domestic combustion can be controlled by :

(a) Appliance selection : Choose vented appliances that have been tested and certified to meet current safety and emission standards.

(b) Proper installation : Improperly installed appliances can release dangerous pollutants, thus they should be installed properly with the help of the experts or the concerned person.

(c) Ventilation : Adequate supply of air is needed to reduce the indoor level of pollutants. This supply of air is also important to help in carrying pollutants upto the chimney, stovepipe or flue to the outside. The appliance should have a vent connected to it. Nothing should block the vent and there should be no holes or cracks in the vent.

(d) Inspection and maintenances : Combustion appliances should be regularly inspected and maintained because appliances that are not working properly can release harmful and even fatal amounts of pollutants, especially carbon monoxide. If air holes of gas stove or gas ranges are blocked, then required amount of oxygen cannot participate in the combustion leading to incomplete combustion.

Kerosene : a desirable cooking fuel inrural areas

Kerosene (also known as paraffin) is a transparent liquid fossil fuel which is generated from the refinement of crude oil. It is highly flammable. Kerosene has been an important household fuel since the mid-19th century. Advancement in science and technology has provided us with various other alternative sources of energy like LPG, electricity, etc. which are user-friendly and economically affordable. However, in many rural areas such advanced sources of energy are not in use. Installation and maintenance of such appliances is difficult in rural areas due to various reasons. Kerosene is often promoted as a cleaner alternative to solid fuels, biomass and coal for cooking.

Advantages of Kerosene as a Cooking Fuel

(a) Food can be cooked faster if cooked in appropriate (pressurised) stoves.

(b) Easy to store.

(c) It is affordable and is available even in smaller quantities.

(d) It is an alternative or back-up source of energy in case of power cuts.

(e) It is an alternative source of energy where access to free biomass for cooking is difficult.

Disadvantages of Kerosene

(a) Kerosene is an exhaustible resource.

(b) Kerosene can produce high levels of pollutants when used in cheap wick stoves leading to significant indoor air pollution.

(c) It has an unpleasant smell and adds an unpleasant taste to the food being cooked.

(d) It is highly flammable. Mishandling and lack of safety measures can cause dangerous hazards.

(e) It's a non-renewable fuel.

Kerosene is not particularly poisonous but repeated exposure to skin may lead to skin inflammation.

? Intext Questions

1. What is combustion?
2. How is kerosene harmful to human body?
3. Why is kerosene preferred as a fuel in rural areas?

(ii) From Industries

Industrialisation aims at providing daily needs of the growing population. These industries use raw materials, process them and produce finished products. Along with the finished products immense amount of pollutants are also generated, which are released into the environment. The gases are usually released into the atmosphere, the liquids are discharged into aquatic bodies like canals, rivers or sea and solid wastes are either dumped on the land or in aquatic bodies. Thus, polluting the air, water or land. A variety of poisonous gases like oxides of nitrogen and sulphur, chlorine, carbon monoxide, carbon dioxide, volatile chemicals, dusts etc. are liberated into the atmosphere causing acute air pollution. These pollutants not only affect the health and life of flora and fauna but also significantly contribute to global warming, acid rain and disturbs the ecological balance and cycles.

Taj Trapezium : Case Study

Taj Mahal, the white marble structure was built by Mughal emperor **Shah Jahan** in the **17th century.** It was declared as the world heritage by UNESCO in 1983. But now the structure has developed yellowish tinge as a result of increased pollution in that area. Taj Mahal is being exposed to sulphur dioxide and Suspended Particulate Matter (SPM). Mathura Oil Refinery which is situated close to that area releases its by-products in the Yamuna river. This has led to acid rain, which is also responsible for damaging the marbles of Taj Mahal. A **Public Interest Litigation (PIL)** was filed in 1984 to express concerns over the havoc caused by such industries. Later, The Supreme Court ordered more than 200 industries in that vicinity to adopt pollution control measures.

Greater emphasis has to be given for the prevention of pollution. These can be implemented and followed to control or reduce industrial air pollution :

(a) Industries must have devices for removal of potential pollutants before the industrial waste is let out to the environment. Scrubbers, closed-collection recovery systems, dry and wet collectors, filters, electrostatic precipitators effectively remove the pollutants.

(b) Taller smoke stacks should be built so that the pollutants do not come in contact with the ground.

(c) Location of the industries should be carefully chosen considering the topography and the wind direction.

(d) Use of eco-friendly and renewable source of energy like wind energy, biomass, solar energy, etc. should be encouraged.

(e) The raw materials that cause pollution should be replaced by eco-friendly, non-polluting or less polluting materials.

(f) Machinery of industries should be maintained and checked for their efficiency regularly. Malfunctioning machineries undergo incomplete combustion of fuel leading to pollution.

(g) Meteorological factor : Air movements influence the fate of air pollutants. If the air is calm and pollutants cannot disperse, then the concentration of these pollutants will build up. But if the turbulent winds blow, pollutants disperse quickly, resulting in lower pollutant concentrations. By identifying the source of pollutants, Meteorological data gives us information about the source of pollutant, and using that information, air quality can be predicted.

(h) Zoning strategies and City planning: This strategy focuses on identifying zones or areas such as residential, agricultural, forest, commercial and industrial. Care should be taken that industries and factories are not built and run in the vicinity of residential, agricultural and forest areas.

(i) The Air (Prevention and Control of Pollution) Act was legislated in 1981. This Act laid down the rules and regulation which aimed at prevention, control and abatement of air pollution. It is strictly vigilant over industrial activities that cause pollution. It is mandatory for industries, constructions, factories to take permission from the **State Pollution Control Boards (SPCB)** to set-up and carry on with their activities. The consent to operate is granted only after it is guaranteed that the activities carried out will not adversely affect the environment by polluting or exhausting it or at least the impact will be under permissible limits.

(j) Subsidies : These are financial assistance granted by a government to a person or a group in support of an enterprise regarded as being in the public interest. Subsidies are given to those industries or business that implement eco-friendly methodologies to carry on their activities. For example–industries which use renewable sources as fuel like solar energy, less or non-polluting raw materials, non-polluting ways of waste disposal, etc. are eligible to receive subsidies from government. By providing such aids government encourages industries and business enterprises to be responsible towards environment.

? Intext Questions

1. Name few eco-friendly renewable sources of energy.
2. Explain the term 'Subsidy' in brief.
3. Which meteorological factors affect air pollution?

Fascinating Fact

The World Bank estimates that air pollution causes a loss of $ 225 billion a year to the global economy.

(iii) From Vehicles

When the fuel is burnt inside the engine of vehicles, pollutants like carbon monoxide, hydrocarbons, oxides of nitrogen, sulphur and lead are released into the air. Since the number of vehicles are increasing all over the world, amount of pollutants is also considerably increasing. Vehicular exhausts release a significant amount of particulates which leads to respiratory disorders. These pollutants contribute to acid rain and global warming as well.

Fascinating Fact

A single bus carries passengers which are likely to drive 40 cars.

Following measures can be implemented to curb air pollution from vehicles :

(a) Catalytic converters : It is an exhaust emission control device that converts toxic gases and pollutants in exhaust gas from an internal combustion engine to less toxic pollutants by catalysing a redox reaction. Installation of catalytic converters can reduce the release of pollutants into the air.

(b) Four stroke engines : Four stroke engines facilitate complete combustion of fuel, hence less pollutants are generated.

(c) Alternative sources of energy like electricity, solar energy, LPG etc. should be used as fuel to run the vehicles. These sources of energy are less polluting.

(d) Actions have to be taken to control the rate of traffic growth. Public awareness and participation in traffic management is a must. Every citizen is equally responsible and accountable for traffic management along with the government.

(e) Using public transports or car-pooling whenever possible can considerably help in reducing pollution. Engines of vehicles can be switched off when we are waiting at the traffic signal. Vehicles should be properly maintained. Ill maintained vehicles emit lots of pollutants.

(f) To regulate the vehicular pollution Central Motor Vehicles Act was laid down. This law notifies and enforces the rules for exhaust emission and mass emission.

SUMMARY

- Pollution is defined as the effect of undesirable change in our surroundings that have harmful effects on plants, animals and human beings.
- Substances which cause pollution are called as **pollutants**
- Air pollution is the addition of harmful substances in air that degrade the air quality
- Air quality is defined as the degree to which the air in a particular place is pollution-free.
- Our daily use appliances like gas ranges, furnaces, gas water heaters, gas clothes dryers, wood or coal-burning stove and fireplaces which use fuels like CNG, LPG, fuel oil, kerosene, wood or coal cause air pollution.
- A variety of poisonous gases like oxides of nitrogen and sulphur, chlorine, carbon monoxide, carbon dioxide, volatile chemicals, dusts etc. are liberated into the atmosphere by industries and vehicles which cause acute air pollution.
- Industries must have devices for removal of potential pollutants before the industrial waste is let out to the environment.
- Meteorological data gives us information about the source of pollutant. Using that information, air quality can be predicted.

- Subsidies are financial assistance granted by a government to a person or group in support of an enterprise regarded as being in the public interest of waste disposal, etc.

A. Define each of these terms :

1. Catalytic converters
2. Meteorological data
3. Air pollution
4. Air quality
5. Pollution
6. Zoning

B. Answer in brief :

1. How would providing subsidies to business help in reducing pollution?
2. Write the word equation to show combustion of fuel.
3. Which are the main pollutants given out by industries and vehicles?
4. Why do poorly maintained appliances release pollutants?
5. What are the devices that industries should have to reduce pollutants from their emission?
6. The height of the smoke stack should be high. Why?
7. How does four stroke engine help in controlling pollution caused by vehicles?
8. How does zoning strategies and city planning help in reducing pollution?
9. What are the legislative actions taken by the government to control the release of pollutants from vehicles?
10. Write any three disadvantages of using kerosene as a cooking fuel.

C. Answer in detail :

1. Despite of availability of variety of user-friendly fuels, Kerosene is widely used in rural areas. Justify the statement.
2. Public awareness and participation can help to a greater extent to control vehicular pollution. Justify the statement.
3. What are the legislative actions taken by the government to control the release of pollutants from industries?
4. List out technological measures that can be undertaken by the industries and factories to control pollution.
5. List out technological measures that can be installed in the vehicles to control pollution.
6. Why did the Supreme Court order more than 200 industries in the vicinity of Taj Mahal to adopt pollution control measures?
7. How does increase in population lead to increase in pollution?
8. Air pollution leads to global warming and acid rain. Justify the statement.

WORKSHEET

A. Fill in the blanks :

1. The abbreviation PAH stands for ______________.
2. A _______ was filed in 1984 by the locals of Delhi against the industries in the vicinity of Taj Mahal.
3. Kerosene is also called as _________.
4. Taj Mahal was declared as World's heritage by ________ in 1983.

B. How can following factors contribute in reducing the air pollution :

1. Meteorological data.
2. Catalytic converters.
3. Scrubbers.
4. Vented home appliances.
5. Inspection and maintenance of home appliances.

C. Read the following excerpts and answer the questions that follow. (Open-ended questions) :

1. A park in the city of Bengaluru witnesses approximately 3 kg of dry leaves fall during the winter season. The park maintainers burn the withered leaves every day.

   (a) Do you agree this is a right way of getting rid of the leaf waste? Justify your answer.

   (b) Suggest a few alternative eco-friendly methods of getting rid of the leaf waste.

2. The Gangotri glaciers are found to be melting due to the global warming, which may bring floods in the nearby villages.

   (a) How is air pollution linked to the global warming?

D. Activities :

1. Interview a traffic police and take information on how many ill maintained vehicles they come across in a day. What measures or actions are taken against it?
2. List out the benefits of four stroke engine over a two-stroke engine.

2 ADDRESSING POPULATION

1.0 INTRODUCTION

Population is defined as the number of living things that live together in the same place. The population includes all individuals that live in that certain area. The world population was estimated to have reached 7.5 billion in April 2017. Asia is the most populated continent, with its 4.3 billion residents making up 60% of the world population. Population growth is the rate at which a population expands. If population growth accelerates faster and larger than the normal, it leads to a condition called overpopulation. Overpopulation is a condition when there are too many organisms of a certain species in a certain habitat. This means that the number of organisms living there is larger than the carrying capacity of the habitat. In the near future scarcity of food, fuel, clean and hygienic soil, water and air will immensely increase. The over exploitation of resources is greatly hampering the buffering action and ability of nature to maintain the ecological balance. These are only some environmental issues that we are likely to face. The current developmental strategies have led to a breakdown of the Earth's ability to replenish the resources on which we depend.

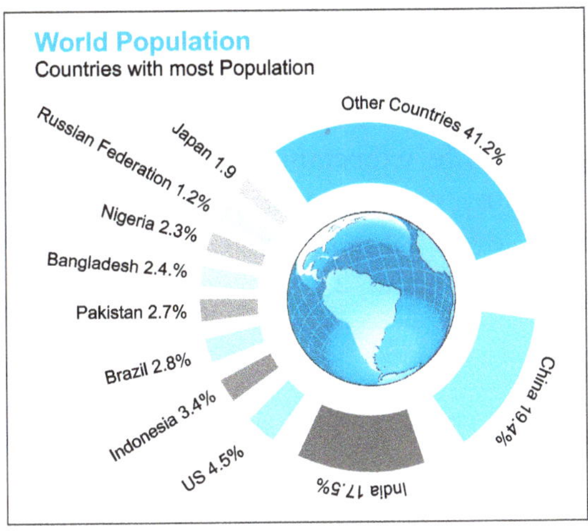

Fascinating Fact

Until 1804, the world population was below a billion. It reached two billion in 1927, three billion in 1960 and four billion in 1974.

1.1 GLOBAL POPULATION GROWTH

200 years ago, there were less than one billion humans living on earth. Today, according to UN calculations there are over 7 billion of us. Recent estimates suggest that today's population size is roughly equivalent to 6.5% of the total number of people ever born. The global human population has immensely increased in the

last 50 years. Various factors like decline in death rate, lack of awareness and education among people in the context of family planning is responsible for overpopulation. The world population is growing by more than 90 million per year. Out of this 97% accounted by the developing countries. Developing countries shelter young population due to which the birth rates go higher. Conversely, in the developed countries the annual number of births barely exceeds deaths because of low birth rates and much older populations. As defined by the United Nations, the developing countries have especially low incomes, high economic vulnerability and poor human development indicators such as low life expectancy at birth, very low per capita income and low levels of education. They are growing at 2.4 percent per year and are projected to reach at least 2 billion by 2050. However, there are cultural, economic, political and demographic reasons that explain the differences in patterns in population growth. The needs of such a huge number of people cannot be supported by natural resources present in our planet. Ability to provide resources and accommodate such a vast population will be beyond carrying capacity of Earth. The carrying capacity is the maximum population size of the species that the environment can sustain indefinitely, given the food, habitat, water and other necessities available in the environment without degrading the quality of human life.

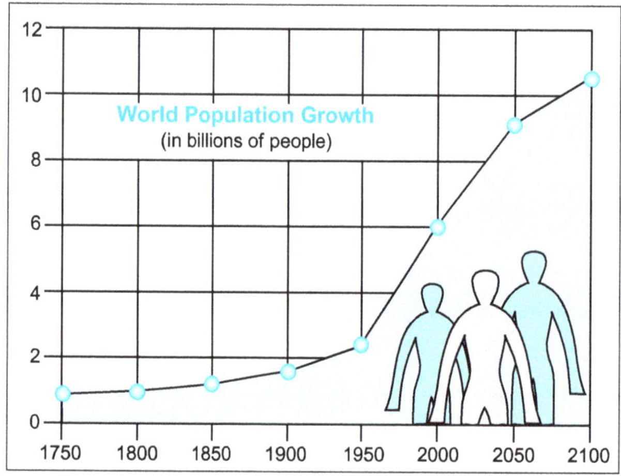

Fascinating Fact

50.4 percent of the world's population is male and 49.6 percent is female. (These figures are subject to change)

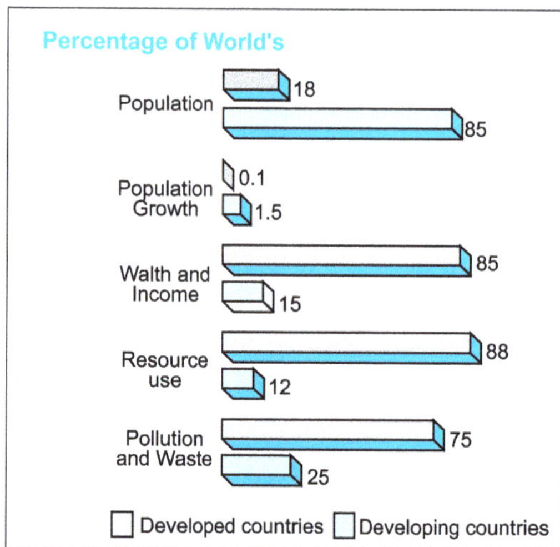

Fascinating Fact

China (1.38 billion) and India (1.33 billion) have the highest populations which means that half the world's population is Chinese or Indian.

1.2 POPULATION EXPLOSION LEADS TO ENVIRONMENTAL DEGRADATION

Increase in population implies to increase in demand for resources which cater to all our needs. It will be impossible to meet the demands for all such needs

like food, fuel, metals, water, shelter, etc. from existing ecosystems. Industries will increase the production of commodities to satisfy the demands that will exhaust all the resources at the faster ate. The effects of population growth on nature are elaborated below :

(a) Industries will pollute the air, water and soil. Chemicals released by industries will also increase global warming and ozone depletion. Biotechnological advancements follow procedures like hybridisation, grafting and focussed cultivation and farming of commercially important plant and animal species. Such steps will hamper the biodiversity and destabilise nature's balance.Developing nations will exploit available resources which may result in extinction of resources, thus making the livelihood of future generations even more difficult.

(b) Natural disasters like earthquake, drought, floods, etc. will occur due to imbalance in nature's bio-geochemical cycles.

(c) Inspite of attempts to cater the needs for immensely growing population, we will still suffer scarcity of quality and quantity of resources.

(d) In rural areas population growth has led to increased fragmentation and unemployment. In urban sector, it has led to inadequate housing, difficulty in planning safe city, inability to handle waste, inability to provide adequate water and electricity supply, massive traffic, etc.

? Intext Questions

1. How does overpopulation cause natural disaster?
2. How will overpopulation affect the carrying capacity of the Earth?

UN Population projection

According to a new UN DESA report, the current world population of 7.3 billion is expected to reach 8.5 billion by 2030, 9.7 billion in 2050 and 11.2

billion in 2100. Most of the projected increase in the world's population can be attributed to a short list of high-fertility countries, mainly in Africa, or countries with already large populations. During 2015-2050, half of the world's population growth is expected to be concentrated in nine countries: India, Nigeria, Pakistan, Democratic Republic of the Congo, Ethiopia, United Republic of Tanzania, United States of America, Indonesia and Uganda, listed according to the size of their contribution to the total growth. India is expected to become the largest country in population size, surpassing China around 2022, while Nigeria could surpass the United States by 2050.

Undoubtedly growing population, implies to more demand for oil, gas, coal and other fuels mined or drilled from below the Earth's surface that, when burned, discharge enough carbon dioxide into the atmosphere to trap warm air inside like a greenhouse.According to the United Nations Population Fund, human population grew from 1.6 billion to 6.1 billion people during the course of the 20th century. During that time emissions of carbon dioxide grew 12-fold. Population, global warming and consumption patterns are linked with collective global environmental impact. Developed countries consume a huge share of fossil fuels and they contribute to large amount of carbon dioxide emission. Even though the population of developed countries has come to a stagnant level, population growth and industrialisation in developing countries is rising rapidly. According to the United Nations Population Fund, fast-growing developing countries (like China and India) will contribute more than half of the global carbon dioxide emissions by 2050.

1.3 THE DEMOGRAPHIC TRANSITIONS

Demographic Transition (DT) refers to the change from high birth and death rates to lower birth and death rates as a country or region develops from a pre-industrial to an industrialised economic system. This theory was proposed by the American demographer Warren Thompson in 1929. He developed this theory after observing transitions in birth and death rates in industrialised societies over the previous 200 years. The demographic transition follows four stages :

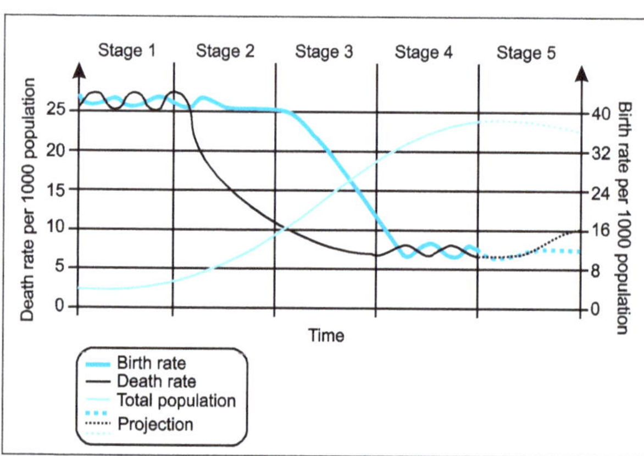

(i) Stage one : This is the earlier stage of demographic transition in the world. In pre-industrial society, death rates and birth rates were both high. It also fluctuated rapidly according to natural events, such as disaster (earthquakes, drought, disease, epidemic, etc.).

(ii) Stage two : This stage leads to a fall in death rates and an increase in population. In the 20th century, the falls in death rates in developing countries tended to be substantially faster. The decline in the death rate is due to two factors :

(a) There were improvements in the food supply brought facilitated by higher yields in agricultural practices and better transportation reduce death due to starvation and lack of water.

(b) There were substantial improvements in public health which reduced mortality. Number of epidemic diseases were reduced due to development of various medicines and vaccines.

(iii) Stage three : In this stage death rates are low and birth rates lessen. Such a condition was observed due to enhanced economic conditions, improved women's status, education and knowledge and access to contraception. The decrease in birth rate fluctuates from nation to nation, as does the time span in which it is experienced.

(iv) Stage four : This stage depicts a stable population where birth and death rates are both low. Death rates are low because of lower rates of diseases and higher production of food. The birth rate is low because people have knowledge and opportunities to choose if they want children. Women have gained more independence and work opportunities. Thus, they can independently make decisions about childbirth. Access to contraception for both men and women has played an important role in decline of birth rate.

The projected rise in the population will be seen in developing countries like India, China, Korea, Malaysia, etc. In contrast, the developed nations like Europe, Northern America, Japan and Australia, population size is forecast to remain virtually stable, growing slightly from 1.22 to 1.25 billion between 2005 and 2050. Developed nations have already stabilised depicting stage four demographic transition. While the developing nations are rapidly undergoing industrialisation, advancements in science and technology and improved status of women. This shows a transition of stage two to stage three in the demography.

? Intext Questions

1. Why are developed nations listed in stage 4 of demography?
2. In the 20th century, the fall in death rates in developing countries tended to be substantially faster. Why?
3. Explain stage one of demographic transition.
4. According to the United Nations Population Fund, fast-growing developing countries (like China and India) will contribute more than half of global carbon dioxide emissions by 2050. Justify the statement.

1.4 STRATEGIES FOR CONTROLLING GROWTH OF POPULATION

Though population growth shows a general global decline, there are variations in the rate of decline in different countries. Some strategies for controlling population growth are mentioned below :

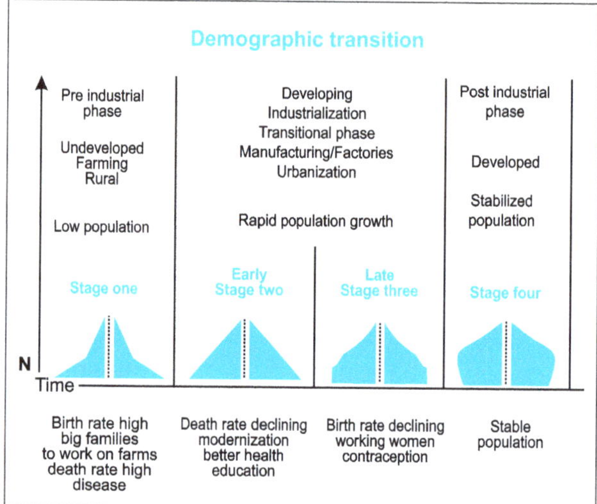

(i) Family planning and birth control: Awareness and knowledge about available contraception methods to the general public is very crucial. The media must highlight the need for limiting family size and ill effects of population growth. Contraception methods for women involves temporary sterilisation (contraceptive pills, IUDs) and permanent sterilisation (tubectomy). Contraception for men involves usage of condoms (temporary sterilisation) and Vasectomy (permanent sterilisation). Appropriate method of contraception should be chosen after consulting a doctor.

(ii) Education and Women-centred Development : The decision to limit family largely depends on a couple's cultural background and education. The idea of limiting family size is counteracted by many cultural attitudes. Such attitudes will change if people are educated. People should be made aware as to how they themselves and whole human race will be affected with such an enormous growing population. People should be made aware of how the quality of life will be much better with less population. Women have legal rights and freedom relating to childbirth and their reproductive health. In most of the male dominating society, women are not aware about obtainability of such right or not empowered to claim their freedom. Some communities and

cultures prohibit use of contraception and/or abortion. Child marriage and forced pregnancy are some of the evil practices which are still going on in many of the backward communities. These evil practices hamper the eminence of next generation of human population. Access to education helps people to understand the importance and need of leaving behind such evil practices. It helps people to respect each other and fosters a positive growth. It is not just enough if we reduce the population, but, the quality of life and livelihood is also vital. A good life cannot be achieved by leaving behind moral and ethical values. Education helps us in developing such values.

Fascinating Fact

Young people ages 10–24 account for about 1.8 billion of the world's population. Ninety percent of them live in developing countries.

(iii) Health care and Economic development : Population growth affects economic development; and in its turn, economic development affects population growth. Economic growth has enabled people to have more money. People are thus able to have access for good life and resources and medical facilities. Therefore, the death rate has declined. But the focus on economic growth is so much that we have been ignoring the fact that overuse of resources for enhancing economy is in turn leading to exhaustion of natural resources. Even the quality of life in terms of hygiene, peace and sanity is deteriorating.

1.5 DEVELOPMENT FRAMEWORK FOR POVERTY ALLEVIATION

Poverty cannot be completely eradicated, as it is a result of lot of factors. However, poverty can be reduced by taking a set of strategic measures. Poverty alleviation, is a set of economic and humanitarian measures that intends to permanently lift people out of poverty. Poverty alleviation involves the strategic use of tools such as education, economic development, health and income redistribution to improve the livelihoods of the world's poorest by governments and internationally approved organizations. They also aim at removing social and legal barriers to income growth among the poor.

Social mobilisation is a participatory process to raise awareness, mobilise and involve local institutions, leadership and communities for collective action towards a common vision. This approach can be used to reduce poverty. It is a process of motivating communities to organise in a cohesive group for an active participation towards their own development. Social Mobilisation is also an integrative process where stakeholders are stimulated to become active participants in social change, using diverse strategies to meet shared goals. Social mobilisation brings together all feasible and partners to raise awareness of and demand for a particular programme, to assist in the delivery of resources and services and to strengthen community participation for sustainability and self-reliance. Social mobilisation approach has yielded positive results in organising poor women into self-help groups and linking them to banks for small credit and thus enabling them to improve their livelihoods. Consequently, concrete social capital has been created among women in the state and social empowerment is on the rise. Following the strategy of social mobilisation SHGs (Self Help Groups) are created with a view of achieving savings mobilization, obtaining credit for emergent requirements, mutual help and economic upliftment through income generating activities. Subsidies are given for starting small scale industries. Small scale industries not only increase the employment opportunity in the rural areas but also give a chance to exhibit their skills and talents.

Precisely, features of social mobilisation can be listed as :

(a) The social mobilisers arrange for mass meeting and encourage them to understand the need to organise for collective action.

(b) Ensure that rules are clearly understood by all group members.

(c) Initially the groups would have to meet daily to discuss the most pressing issues and action to be taken.

(d) For a community, the appropriate number of groups would be around 20.

(e) Primary Groups meetings are used to activate and motivate passive member.

Human development is yet another strategy to reduce poverty. Human development is defined as the process of enlarging people's freedom and opportunities for improving their well-being. Human development aims at expanding human capabilities. Human Development Index (HDI) measures life expectancy, education and per capita income for countries worldwide. It aims at ensuring access to education, training and raising public awareness as essential for social progress and improving the capacity of people. Poverty eradication and capacity enhancement programmes are organised and monitored by ministries, departments, NGOs, Panchayati Rajs, etc. Approaches to poverty mitigation will be effective if appropriate steps are taken at local, national as well as global level.

SUMMARY

- Population is defined as the number of living things that live together in the same place.
- The global human population has immensely increased in the last 50 years. Various factors like decline in death rate, lack of awareness and education among people in the context of family planning is responsible for overpopulation.

- Scarcity of resources, disturbance in nature balance, natural disasters, pollution, unemployment, inadequate housing, difficulty in planning safe city, inability to handle waste, inability to provide adequate water and electricity supply, massive traffic are some of the effects of overpopulation.
- Demographic transition (DT) refers to the change from high birth and death rates to lower birth and death rates as a country or region develops from a pre-industrial to an industrialised economic system.
- Family planning, education, women empowerment, increasing awareness, eradication of social evils like child marriage are some measure to control population growth.
- Full-fledged poverty alleviation can be achieved by taking measures such as human development, social mobilisation, empowering poor people by setting up SHGs, small scale industries, educating them, etc.
- Social mobilisation is a participatory process to raise awareness, mobilize and involve local institutions, leadership and communities for collective action towards a common vision.
- Human development is defined as the process of enlarging people's freedom and opportunities for improving their well-being.

A. Define each of these terms :

1. Overpopulation
2. Poverty alleviation
3. Carrying capacity

B. Answer in brief :

1. List the factors contributing to overpopulation.
2. Why is population growth in developing countries is more compared to developed nations?
3. How is overpopulation affecting carrying capacity of the Earth?
4. How has overpopulation affected rural and urban areas?
5. Describe the role of media in limiting population growth.
6. How does cultural background and education affect population growth?
7. How are economic development and population growth related to each other?

C. Answer in detail :

1. Explain all the stages of demographic transitions in brief.
2. How does social mobilisation help in poverty alleviation?
3. Human development is a key to eradicate poverty. Justify the statement.
4. How do social evils result in overpopulation?
5. What is the impact of population on the land?

D. Previous Years Board Questions :

1. Define demographic transitions
2. State two factors responsible for population explosion.
3. Enumerate various strategies adopted to control population.
4. What do you mean by social mobilisation? Mention any four of its features.

WORKSHEET

A. Fill in the blanks :

1. The most populated continent is _______
2. The first theory of demography was developed by _______ .
3. The participatory process to involve the society and local institutions towards the accomplishment of a common vision is called _______ .
4. _______ measures life expectancy, education and per capita income for countries worldwide.

B. Justify the following statements :

1. 97% of the accounted population resides in the developing nations.
2. The population in the developed nation is stable.
3. Women empowerment is one of the essential factors to combat the overpopulation problems.
4. Population growth affects economic development; and in turn, economic development affects population growth
5. The role of media is significant in population control.

C. Read the following excerpts and answer the questions that follow. (open-ended questions) :

(1) Canada is regarded as the underpopulated country. Its carrying capacity is much higher than its population. The 38 million people in Canada cannot fully exploit the available resources.

(a) List out the problems that the country might face due to underpopulation.

(2) China is a habitat for 20% of the world's population. In 1979, the government released the policy called 'one family one child'. This policy was accompanied by encouragement to the citizens in the form of prize, subsidies, scholarship to the child, etc.

(a) List out the advantages and the disadvantages of this policy.

(3) Japan is one of the densely populated countries. However, the uneven distribution of population is also seen in Japan. Very few people live on the mountainous slopes in the centre of Honshu island and the south of Shikoku island.

(a) List out the probable reasons for low population density in the Honshu island and the Shikoku island.

D. Activities :

(1) Study the population pattern in one of the rural areas near your locality. Your observation must include the following data. Also draw a pie chart for the data obtained in (a and b).

(a) Approximate number of males and females.

(b) Approximate number of people of different age group (0-5, 5-10, 10-25, 25-45, 45-65, 65 and above).

(c) Approximate number of people migrated from that area to the city in the past 5 years.

(2) Write down 5 slogans or quotes to convince women empowerment for the betterment of our society. Enact a short skit on the same topic.

3 MANAGING THE URBAN ENVIRONMENT

1.0 INTRODUCTION

Since in the 19th century a rapid growth in technology and economy is seen. Such a development has induced urbanisation. Urbanisation has become a common feature and outcome of economic development. Urbanisation refers to the population shift from rural to urban areas and the ways in which society adapts to the changes. It is basically the process by which towns and cities are formed and become larger as more people begin living and working in central areas. By the early 1900s Great Britain and the United States had become predominantly urbanised nations; since that time, urbanisation has been occurring around the globe at a rapid rate. It is predicted that by 2050 about 64% of the developing world and 86% of the developed world will be urbanised. Notably, the United Nations has also recently projected that nearly all global population growth from 2017 to 2030 will be absorbed by cities, about 1.1 billion new urbanites over the next 13 years. Urbanisation is not merely shifting of rural human population to urban areas but also implies to replacing rural culture with the urban culture. Due to social and economic pressures, people from rural areas migrate to urbanised centres in search of job. But, urbanisation has however lead to a large number of problems in urban areas like over and unbalanced population, scarcity of resources and shelter, poor traffic management, huge waste generation, pollution, unhygienic conditions, ill-health etc.

Planning and building sustainable cities is the need of the hour. These measures can be implemented to manage urban areas :

(i) Efficient land use

(ii) Planning resource and energy usage

(iii) Traffic management

(iv) Waste management

(v) Maintaining city hygiene

(vi) Participation and contribution from citizens or residents.

1.1 SUSTAINABLE CITIES

A sustainable city is a city designed by considering environmental impact. It is inhabited by people dedicated towards minimized and optimal resource

use (energy, food, water, etc), reduced waste generation and activities that cause pollution. Sustainable city also aims at creating a pleasant life across the domains like environment, technology, economy and culture. A sustainable city can be achieved through various means like :

(i) Efficient land use and city planning

With the increased rate of urbanisation, city planning is very crucial to accommodate the huge population. It is a process which aims to develop and use of land, involvement of concerned authorities, protection and use of the environment, public welfare and the design of the urban environment, including air, water and the infrastructure passing into and out of urban areas, such as transportation, communication and distribution networks. Urban planning includes techniques such as predicting population growth, zoning, geographic mapping and analysis, analysing park space, surveying the water supply, identifying transportation patterns, recognising food supply demands, allocating healthcare and social services, and analysing the impact of land use. Urban planners plan for the development and management of urban and suburban areas by considering all the appropriate criteria. Such a comprehensive planning is required to build well equipped and aesthetical city.

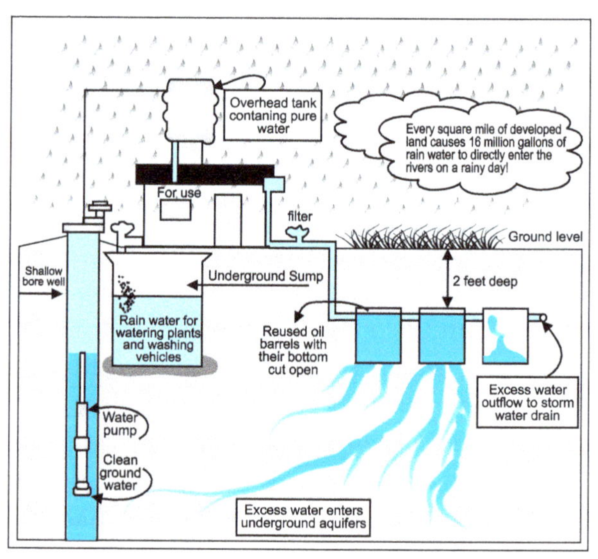

Fascinating Fact

Denmark is cycle loving country. It ranks second with most cycle per capita after Netherlands in the world. In Denmark 18% of all trips are made by bike.

(ii) Resource planning (food, water and energy)

(a) Food

There are hardly any land available for growing plants in cities. Therefore, the staple food products like vegetables, fruits, pulses, grains, etc. are imported from nearby agricultural areas. During transportation, considerable food products are spoiled especially the perishable food products. This leads to food wastage. If there are agricultural plots in the cities, some crops can be grown in the city itself. This reduces the distance food has to travel from field to city.

(b) Water

In urban areas, the construction of houses, footpaths and roads has left little exposed earth for water to soak in. Therefore, there is hardly any scope for groundwater recharge, therefore city planners and authorities have introduced various measures for reducing water consumption and conservation as follows :

1. Litres of water can be saved if we follow some best practices like turn off the tap when not in use, installation of low flow shower heads and low flow toilet flushes, wash only a full when using the washing machine.

2. Rainwater harvesting is a very popular method of conserving water especially in the urban areas. Rainwater harvesting means collecting rainwater on the roofs of building and storing it underground for later use. This method raises the declining water table, recharges groundwater and can help augment water supply.

(c) Energy

Most of the energy sources that we use are either non-renewable or take a very long time to replenish. Therefore, judicious use of such resources is essential. Following measures can be followed to save energy :

1. Zero Energy Building is a building with zero net energy consumption, meaning the total amount of energy used by the building on an annual basis is roughly equal to the amount of renewable energy created on the site. These buildings consequently contribute less overall greenhouse gas.

2. Solar energy is a renewable, inexhaustible and clean source of energy. Usage of solar appliances wherever appropriate should be encouraged. Energy can be conserved by reducing wastage and losses, improvement in efficiency by technological upgradation and improved operation and maintenance. Regular servicing of vehicles, usage of LED bulbs, turning on energy save mode in air conditioners, using renewable energy sources, such as wind turbines, solar panels or bio-gas created from sewage are some ways to conserve energy.

(iii) Transportation and Traffic management

Managing traffic in cities is a huge challenge. Problems such as congestion, road capacity, networks, and pollution are difficult to combat. Incapability of managing traffic is leading to problems like pollution and unsafe conditions, accidents, etc. Below listed are some measures that can be followed to combat traffic and transportation issues.

1. Set-up well planned and dense public transport facilities like bus, trams, metro, train, ferry, etc. public transport facilities should be commutable to all areas of the city.

2. Encourage use of bicycles and pedestrianisation instead to scooters and bikes within the city.

3. Encourage car-pooling.

4. Proper city planning with clearly differentiated business, industrial and residential zones.

Fascinating Fact

In some countries like USA, Australia and New Zealand, there are desinated lanes called HOV (High Occupancy Vehicle) lanes, which are meant to be used only by those who are carpooling and are designed the travel time faster.

5. It should be made mandatory for all the buildings (apartments, hospitals, shopping malls, theatres, etc.) to have a parking space, so that people do not park their vehicles on roads, thus reducing congestion on roads.

6. Traffic policies and rules should be made and followed. Stringent actions should be taken on violation of traffic rules.

Intext Questions

1. What do you understand by the term Zero Energy Building?
2. Why is scope for groundwater recharge less in cities?
3. What is rainwater harvesting?

(iv) Waste Management

The population growth within cities has resulted in increasing quantities of waste being generated. The negative impacts of wastes are evident on the quality of air, water, land, human health, etc. Thus, an integrated approach to waste management is must. The 3Rs principle (reduce, reuse and recycle) approach is the key to waste management.

(a) Reduce

The concept of reducing what is produced and what is consumed is first step to waste management. If there is less waste, then there is less to recycle or reuse. The process of reducing can be done by examining what we are using and what it is used for. For example, use both side of the paper for printing or writing, planning the purchase list, avoid disposable plates, spoons, glasses wherever possible, etc.

(b) Reuse

The next step is reuse. We should try to reuse the items or re-purpose them for a different use. For example – empty plastic soft drink or water bottles can be decorated and made into show-pieces or pen stand, old damaged jars can be refurbished and used as planters, processed food containers can be used for storing items, etc.

(c) Recycle

In this step, materials are recycled such that it will be transformed again into a raw material that can be shaped into a new item. Materials made up of glass, plastic, paper, metals can be recycled to get back the raw material, which can be further used to make new products.

(v) Solid Waste Management

Garbage disposal and handling is yet another challenge in urban areas. Due to lack of proper systems, procedure and facilities, garbage is dumped in inappropriate places. Such an unhygienic condition not only cause inconvenience but also give rise to various types of infection and diseases. Some steps to smoothen solid waste management is as follows :

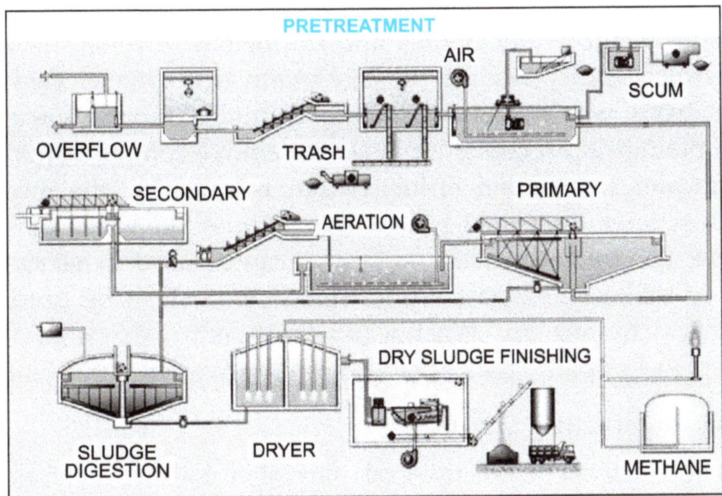

(a) Segregation of waste at the source is the key to waste management. Solid waste should be separated as biodegradable waste, non-biodegradable waste, electronic waste, etc.

(b) No person is allowed to throw, burn or bury the solid waste generated by him, on streets, open public spaces outside his premises, or in the drain, or water bodies.

(c) Every street vendor should keep suitable containers for storage of waste generated during the course of his or her activity such as food waste, disposable plates, cups, cans, wrappers, coconut shells, leftover food, vegetables, fruits etc. and deposit such waste at waste storage depot or container or vehicle as notified by the local authority.

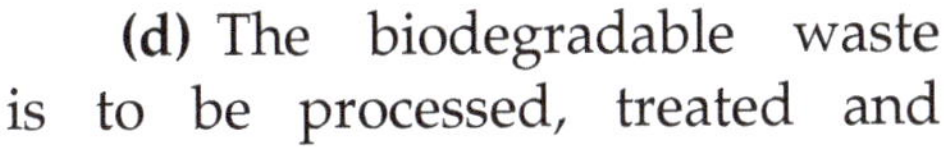

(d) The biodegradable waste is to be processed, treated and disposed of through composting or bio-methanation within the premises as far as possible. The non-biodegradable waste like plastic, metal, glass, etc. should be recycled.

(e) The waste generated by hospitals should be disposed in a specific manner as laid down by government rules. Hospital waste should not be mixed with domestic waste.

(f) Sewage system

According to the Census, only one–third of urban houses in India are connected to the sewer system. The majority of the houses have toilets connected to septic tanks. The quality of the septic tanks, buried underground in populated areas, is often poor. As a result, the treatment of sewage is partial. Then there is no system for the disposal of the faecal sludge, which is in most cases emptied out surreptitiously into water bodies and municipal sewers. The waste should be treated first before disposing it. Sewage treatment is the process of removing contaminants from wastewater, primarily from household sewage. Physical, chemical and biological processes are used to remove contaminants and produce treated wastewater (or treated effluent) that is safer for the environment. A by-product of sewage treatment is usually a semi-solid waste or slurry, called sewage sludge. The treated water and sludge can be used in agriculture. Sludge can be used to make a compost while treated water can be used in watering plants, cleaning activities, etc. Wastewater treatment is essential as it prevents growth and spread of pathogens arising out of unhygienic condition.

(v) Planning construction activities

Construction activity is an integral part of a country's infrastructure and industrial development. It includes hospitals, schools, townships, offices, houses and other buildings, urban infrastructure (including water supply, sewerage, drainage), highways, roads, ports, railways, airports, power systems; irrigation and agriculture systems, tele-communications etc. Energy, materials, water and land are all consumed in the construction and operation of buildings and infrastructure. These built structures in turn become part of our living environment, affecting our living conditions, social well-being and health. It is therefore important to explore environmentally and economically sound design and development techniques in order to design buildings and infrastructure that are sustainable, healthy and affordable. Therefore, infrastructure and the environment are inseparably linked. Sustainable urban infrastructure is the one where attention is paid to technological and government policy which

enables urban planning for sustainable architecture and initiatives that promote sustainable agriculture. Following are the criteria of sustainable infrastructure :

(a) Identification of zones of city such as residential, agricultural, forest, commercial and industrial.

(b) Integrated resource (food, water, energy) management .

(c) Permitting construction of only green buildings or eco-friendly buildings.

(d) Strict adherence to environment protocol.

(e) Proper handling and disposal of waste generated during construction activity.

? Intext Questions

1. Define sludge.
2. What is meant by sewage treatment?
3. What is meant by sustainable infrastructure?

1.2 RURAL DEVELOPMENT

Since the 19th century population shifting from rural to urban areas has immensely increased. Throughout history, one of the most effective strategies for people to look for a better future has been to migrate. Some of the reasons which influence relocation of people from rural areas to cities are :

(a) Technological advancements in urban areas create a lot of job opportunities. One of the major reasons for relocation of people is to get appropriate and desired job. Better job opportunities also ensure financial stability.

(b) Cities have better education facilities and quality compared to the rural areas. There are lots of options for various courses of different subjects.

(c) The healthcare or medical reasons are yet another reason for migration to urban areas. Advanced medical facilities are available in cities.

(d) Residents of city lead a modern, comfortable and lucrative lifestyle as they have access to various facilities like appliances, gadgets, etc. Many rural areas lack basic needs like regular electricity supply, telephone or mobile network coverage, etc.

Over urbanisation has caused unbalanced distribution of population, which in turn is leading to various problems like :

(a) Shortage of resources and space in urban areas.

(b) Decline in quality of environment and life in urban areas.

(c) Unemployment.

(d) Lack of motivation and interest in rural areas to practice agriculture.

(e) Lack of interest and motivation to practice indigenous and exotic occupations like pottery, carving, sculpture making, etc, which are representatives of our culture and tradition.

Rural-Urban migration has detrimental effects on village as well as city economy, culture and quality of life. Extensive urbanisation is causing an imbalance. Rural development is the key to combat such an imbalance and its consequences.

One of the major causes for the rising migration from rural to urban areas is lack of productive employment, creating earning opportunities by generating sufficient number of jobs and business opportunities in rural areas would be the best way to stop people from migrating.

(a) Every village in our country should be provided with basic amenities like clean drinking water, irrigation facilities for crops, uninterrupted power supply, modern communication network and internet access.

(b) There are no colleges and higher education facilities in many of the villages. The schools in village lack basic amenities. Quality educational institutes should come up in village areas.

(c) Clinics, dispensaries and hospitals in rural areas are not well equipment to treat all types of diseases. Sound hospitals with qualified medical professionals should come up in villages, so that, there is no need for villagers to visit or to relocate to cities for treatment.

(d) Rural areas should be provided with good public transport facilities.

(e) Most jobs in rural areas are agriculture related or dependent on agriculture. They often tend to be seasonal and therefore unreliable. For the rural masses to overcome poverty, villages should be able to provide economic opportunities throughout the year. Small scale industries that can be linked with agricultural operations spread over rural areas and smaller towns nearby should be set-up. For this to happen, our government should promote economic prospects and focus on infrastructure development in rural areas. It should also create ready markets for supporting agricultural and economic activities and also development of sustainable agricultural practices in the rural sector.

(f) Other sources of income like eco-tourism should be encouraged. Even indigenous and exotic skills and art forms in the form of entertainment (folk dance and song), art and crafts (paintings, handicrafts, pottery, sculptures, cloth embroidery, etc.) should be encouraged and advertised. This attracts tourists from other countries also and fetches a good amount of earnings to the business owners.

1.3 SECONDARY CITIES

Secondary city describes the second level in the hierarchy of cities below the primary level. Secondary cities play an important role as secondary hubs in facilitating the localized production, transportation, transformation or transfer of goods, people, trade, information, and services between sub-national, metropolitan, national, regional, and global systems of cities. The growth of secondary cities signals the diversification of economic activity, as well as a more equitable distribution of the benefits of development. A secondary city will likely have a population or economy ranging in size between 10% and 50% of a nation's largest city. According to survey, one hundred million people are moving to cities in the next 10 years. If this huge population are accommodated into second-tier cities instead of migrating to First-tier cities, saturation pressure in cities will be considerably reduced. Technological and infrastructural development has to happen in secondary cities too, so that people are motivated to relocate to secondary cities. This will bring about balanced spread of population, instead of over populating and over exhausting few cities. Development of secondary cities fosters availability of resources, functioning of governing bodies and organisation, quality of services like medical or educational, employment opportunities, quality of infrastructure and quality of environment. All these improvements in turn will enhance economic development. According to the World Bank, secondary cities make up almost 40% of the world cities population. They form an important part of an emerging global system of cities. The large cities play a significant role in shaping the new economic geography of cities in fostering global trade, travel and investment, it is secondary cities which will have a much stronger influence in the future upon the economic development of countries. The quality of life in terms of peace and harmony will also be improved.

1.4 COMMUNITY PARTICIPATION AND CONTRIBUTION OF PRIVATE ENTERPRISES

Community participation for keeping the surroundings clean :

A clean city provides not only a good ambience but also disease and pollution free, and a safe habitat for its residents. However, it is not only the responsibility of governing bodies like municipality to maintain city cleanliness. Contribution given by community, private sectors and each resident is significant. Following are the strategies to keep our surrounding clean :

(a) A sense of responsibility towards maintaining our surroundings and city should be developed in all residents. Education at school and home plays a vital role in creating awareness and understanding the importance of city hygiene. Each resident can take simple steps like throwing waste in the waste bins and not littering on the floor, use public toilets, segregated waste created in our house as bio-degradable waste and non-biodegradable waste, install proper soak pits for sanitary waste so that the waste does not spread out to the surrounding, etc. These steps rather prevent city from contamination.

(b) As a community, we should start cleanliness campaigns with an agenda of not only cleaning the city but also spreading awareness about personal and city hygiene. These campaigns motivate and influences ever more people to join. Such a progressive involvement of huge number of people ensures good results.

(c) Private enterprises are organisations like industries, factories, restaurants, hospitals, educational institutes, shopping malls, theatres, etc. The private sector provides a considerable percentile of employment including formal and informal jobs. Private sectors play a crucial role in urban governance. They influence whether urban areas develop in inclusive and sustainable ways, affect poverty reduction and along with the economic development. Their activities generate a huge amount of waste and cause pollution (air, water, soil and sound) which are not handled in an appropriate way. Therefore, it is critical to involve private sectors also in city development. Interactive planning and decision-making processes are needed to support private sector participation in urban governance and to co-ordinate with municipalities. Following measures can be undertaken to enhance private enterprise participation :

1. Incentives and appreciation can be given to encourage private sector participation.

2. Implement specific policies and interventions that complement, coordinate and collaborate with the private sector.

3. In fostering partnerships, munici-palities need to build relations with local and foreign private sector interests by involving associations and companies in city-wide strategic planning processes.

A holistic approach, strategy and contri-bution given by the government, private sectors and every resident is essential for overall urban development.

SUMMARY

- Since the 19th century a rapid growth in technology and thus economy is seen. Such a development has induced urbanisation.
- Urbanisation refers to the population shift from rural to urban areas and the ways in which society adapts to the changes.
- A sustainable city can be built by taking appropriate measures on land planning, resource planning, traffic management, city hygiene, waste management and traffic management.
- By developing rural areas and secondary cities we can combat the ill-effects and imbalance caused by over urbanisation.
- Participation form government, private sectors, communities and citizens is required for progressive development and upgradation in the city.
- The 3Rs principle is the key to waste management.
- Unbalanced population distribution caused by over urbanisation has led to various problems like unemployment, scarcity of resources, reduction in number of people practicing agriculture and indigenous occupations.
- Rural-Urban migration has detrimental effects of village as well as city economy, culture and quality of life.

A. Define each of these terms :

1. Urbanisation
2. Sustainable development
3. Secondary cities

B. Answer in brief :

1. Give the characteristic features of sustainable development.
2. Give four features of secondary cities.
3. Why urban planning is needed ? Explain.
4. Give three factors which effect the development of secondary cities.
5. What is the importance of sanitary and wastewater development ?

C. Answer in the following in detail :

1. Resource planning is a good step towards achieving sustainable city. Justify.
2. How can we enhance participation from private sectors to enhance city development ?
3. What are the contributions a citizen can make to keep his/her city clean ?
4. How do secondary cities help in countering migration ?
5. List out the various problems occurring due to over urbanisation.
6. List out the criteria for sustainable infrastructure.

D. Previous Years Board Questions :

1. State any two advantages of land planning.
2. How has slowing down of economic growth created hardship for the urban poor ?
3. Name the three 'Rs' and explain any one of them.
4. List any two benefits of an MNC that influences the growth of developing nations.
5. How can private enterprise contribute towards city improvement ?
6. What measures can be taken to improve traffic circulation ?
7. State one advantage and one disadvantage of sewage sludge.
8. What are biodegradable wastes ? How are they useful ?

WORKSHEET

A. Fill in the blanks :

1. The _______ refers to the population shift from rural to urban areas and the ways in which society adapts to the changes.
2. The semi solid by-product of the sewage treatment is called _____
3. _______ is a process by which organic material is microbiologically converted under anaerobic conditions to biogas.

B. State any two ways of handling the following issues :

1. Garbage accumulation on the road.
2. Unemployment in the rural areas.
3. Saturation in the cities.
4. Food resource planning in cities.

C. Read the following excerpts and answer the questions that follow. (open-ended questions) :

1. Urbanisation is not merely shifting of rural human population to urban areas but also implies to replacing rural culture with the urban culture.
   (a) Justify the statement.
2. In the last 5 years, National Highways Authority of India have started and accomplished many Highway road construction projects in many states of India.
   (a) List out the sustainable infrastructure criteria that should be taken care of while starting the road construction project.

D. Activities :

1. Plan and make a report on the implementation of 3R principle for management of your kitchen waste.
   (a) Interview a traffic police and collect the following information : approximate number of faulty and under-maintained vehicles that they come across every day; the type of action or penalty levied on the owners of faulty and under-maintained vehicles.

4 MANAGING SOIL AND LAND

1.0 INTRODUCTION

Soil is a vital part of our nature. Soil is a mixture of organic matter, minerals, gases, liquids and organisms that together support life. Soil interfaces with the lithosphere, the hydrosphere, the atmosphere and the biosphere. Agents like wind, water, heat and plants cause weathering of rocks, thus forming the soil. Gravel, sand, silt, water and humus are all constituents of soil. It is essential for life, in the sense that they provide the medium for plant growth, habitat for many insects and other organisms, act as a filtration system for surface water, carbon store and maintenance of atmospheric gases. It would be impossible to initiate the food chain without soil. Only 25 percent of the earth's surface is made up of soil and only 10 percent of that soil can be used to grow food. Therefore, it is crucial to maintain the quality of soil. Owing to various human activities, the quality of soil is degrading. Soil degradation can be defined as a process by which one or more of the potential ecological functions of the soil are harmed. This process lowers the current and/or future capacity of the soil to produce goods and services. Soil degradation can be either a result of natural hazards or due to unsuitable land use and inappropriate land management practices.

Fascinating Facts

The main food grain of India is rice. India ranks second worldwide in rice production.

1.1 CONSERVING SOIL

Soil is the foundation of life and of civilisation on this planet. Soil formation is a long slow process. It's estimated that an inch of soil takes 500 to 1000 years to form.Soil is being lost at rates much faster than it can reasonably be sustained or built. One of the major reasons for soil degradation is soil erosion. Soil erosion is the displacement of the upper layer of soil. The agents of soil erosion are water and wind. Over-use, deforestation, salinisation and chemical contamination are the major factors responsible for soil loss and loss of soil fertility. A significant amount of soil is lost each year. Soil is being swept and washed away 10 to 40 times faster than it is being replenished. A 2008 report entitled "Global soil degradation" estimated that land degradation affects *38% of the world's cropland*. Hence, taking measures to mitigate soil erosion is essential.

Fascinating Facts

Soil is alive with microbes and bugs which play an important role in cycling nutrients in a symbiotic relationship with plants. Chemical fertilizers can add a few nutrients to the soil, it cannot emulate the complex nutritional role of microorganisms.

Erosion control techniques

(i) **Terrace farming :** A sloped plane is cut into a series of flat surfaces or platforms, which resemble steps. Terrace farming is practiced in mountains areas. It is an effective method to control erosion and surface run-off. The speed of the running or flowing water is interrupted when it flows through steps.Terrace farming can be used to grow crops like rice, which requires irrigation.

(ii) **Contour farming :** In contour ploughing, the land is ploughed across or perpendicular to the slopes and along the contour lines. The ruts made by the contours result in furrows that curve around the land. The slopes length shortens, slowing down the water flow. Therefore, water can soak into the soil. Contour ploughing not only controls soil erosion but also improves soil profile by creating a water break.

(iii) **Dry farming :** In this method, the crops which do not have high water requirement are chosen. Dry farming, therefore, is a method of farming without irrigation. Alternative options like planting drought-resistant crops, employing moisture-enhancing techniques such as planting seeds deep in the ground or using and maintaining a fine surface tilth or mulch that delays evaporation, is taken up. In dry areas, upper layers of the soil are usually dehydrated due to exposure to sunlight. However, moisture is retained in below layers of the soil. Seeds are planted in lower layers of the soil to help the germination process.Mulches are materials like cut branches and grass, straw, leaves, etc. Such materials can be put on soil to reduce evaporation.

(iv) Building bunds : Bunds are embankments or a cause way. There are two types of bunds *i.e.*, the contour bunds and the semi-circular bunds. Contour bunds are built using stones down the slope. Semi-circular bunds are made by digging small pits. By building bunds along the contour lines, water runoff is slowed down, which leads to increased water infiltration and enhanced soil moisture. Bunds are usually constructed either with soil or stones.

(v) Removing or patching gullies : Gullies are a ravine formed by the action of water. Excessive clearing, inappropriate land use and overgrazing are all factors leading to the formation of gully. Proper land management and use strategy is must to control such scenarios. Gully erosion occurs when water is channelled across unprotected land and washes away the soil along the drainage lines. Such gullies should be patched. Alternatively, installation of pipe lines or planting grass can also prevent gully erosion.

(vi) Wind breakers : A windbreak is a plantation usually made up of one or more rows of trees or shrubs planted in such a manner so as to provide shelter from the wind and to protect soil from erosion. They are commonly planted in hedgerows around the edges of fields on farms. These are rows of trees and shrubs that are planted along the edges of agricultural fields, to shield the fields against winds. Wind breakers not only significantly reduce wind erosion but also enhance air quality and aesthetic appearance of the fields. Big trees have strong and dense network of roots. Hence, they hold soil tightly and reduce soil erosion caused by flowing water.

(vii) Usage of organic manure : Organic manures are natural fertilizers which are obtained from sources like animal excreta, plant waste, crop residues, etc. Manures increase soil fertility by adding various macro-nutrients and micro-nutrients like Nitrogen, Potassium, Phosphorous, Zinc, etc. Manures easily decompose under the soil. Unlike chemical fertilizers, manures do not affect the microbes and worms residing in the soil. Addition of organic manure contributes to improved soil structure, resulting in improved water infiltration and greater water-holding capacity. Thus, soil erosion is reduced.

? Intext Questions

1. How do big trees act as wind-breakers?
2. What is dry farming?

1.2 SOIL CONSERVATION TECHNIQUES

Soils are essential for the continuity of life on earth since many ecosystems depend on them for survival. Human activities like use of chemical pesticides and herbicides, unsustainable agricultural practices, excessive farming, water pollution and land pollution has resulted in severe degradation of soil quality and natural function in the soil. Soil conservation is the practice of protecting the soil against erosion or deterioration. It involves the activities that can be undertaken to ensure our soils are at their optimum quality and health.

(i) Land use management : It is the process of managing the use and development of land resources in both urban and rural areas. Land is used for various activities like agriculture, construction, forestry, etc. The study of soil profile and climatic conditions should be done before deciding which activity is to be carried on that particular land.The choice of appropriate crops should be done based on the soil profile and climatic conditions. Activities like deforestation, over-exploitation and construction are eventually resulting in soil degradation. Such activities should be carried out in a sustainable manner.

(ii) Vegetative Practices : There are two means of vegetative methods for soil conservation :

(a) Agronomic practices : Agronomic practices are steps farmers incorporate into their farm management systems to improve soil quality, enhance water use, manage crop residue and improve the environment through better fertilizer management. These include contour farming, tillage, crop rotation, mulching and strip cropping.

(b) Agrostological methods : Cultivation of grass in a land which is heavily eroded is called an agrostological measure. These are of two types. In ley farming grass is cultivated in rotation with regular crops. This helps in soil protection as well as produce fodder to cattle. If a land is heavily eroded it is best to allow it to the growth of grasses for few years. This will help in the checking of erosion.

(iii) Mechanical practices : The mechanical practices of soil conservation include various engineering techniques and structures. Mechanical methods for soil conservation are:

(a) Basin Leaching : In this method, a number of small basins (water reservoirs) are made along the contour. Basins collect and retain rain water for long period and also catch and stabilize downwardly moving soils of the slopes.

(b) Contour terracing : The drainage channels, ridges or soil mounds are formed along the contour at right angles to the slope to retain water in the soil and check the soil erosion. These are called terraces which reduce soil erosion.

(c) Sub-soiling : In this method hard sub-soil is broken. This process promotes absorption of rain water and makes the soil looser and fit to allow flourishing growth of vegetation.

(d) Pan-breaking : In some areas, soils become impervious to water and are less productive because of formation of hard sheet of clay. Such areas can be made productive and water permeable by breaking hard clay pans. By pan breaking, drainage and percolation of rain water is improved and soil is saved from residual run-off and erosion.

(iv) Cropping systems : Implementation of appropriate cropping system can contribute a lot in retaining top soil and enhancing the soil profile and quality.

(a) Strip cropping : This is an agricultural practice of cultivating different crops in alternate strips to prevent soil erosion. Strip cropping helps to stop soil erosion by creating natural dams for water, helping to preserve the strength of the soil. Certain layers of plants will absorb minerals and water from the soil more effectively than others. Therefore, the farmland stays fertile much longer.

(b) Tree copping : Soil holding and water absorbing capacity of trees is higher than shrubs of plants. The roots of trees penetrate deep inside the soil, making soil loose. As the roots of tree hold the soil, there are very less chances for soil erosion through flowing water or blow wind. Trees not only prevent topsoil run-off but also contribute in soil formation by weathering below layers of soil, which eventually results in improved soil profile.

(v) Integrated measures to conserve soil and water : There are always strong links between measures for soil conservation and measures for water conservation, and this applies equally in semi-arid areas. Soil and water conservation are those activities at the local level which maintain or enhance the productive capacity of the land including soil, water and vegetation in areas prone to degradation through prevention or reduction of soil erosion, compaction, salinity, conservation or drainage of water and maintenance or improvement of soil fertility. Some of the ways are detailed below –

(a) Increasing water absorption capacity : Crop roots slows down the top soil run-off. Earthworms and other soil life maintain cracks and pores in the soil. Less water runs off and more sinks into the soil. Ripped furrows and planting basins collect and store water.

(b) Preventing over-tillage : The crop cover protects soil from drying out due to less exposure to heat from sun and blowing wind. Thus, water can sink deep in the soil.

(c) Seeds should be sown at the right time : If seeds are sown just before the onset of monsoon season, huge amount of water can be saved as there will be no need for artificial irrigation.

? Intext Questions

1. Why is land planning essential for preventing soil degradation?
2. How does over tillage lead to soil degradation?
3. What is strip cropping?

1.3 LAND REFORMS

In India, prior to independence Zamindars or the land owners held enormous agricultural lands and control over their peasants, from whom they reserved the right to collect tax on behalf of the King or talukdars. This system was abolished when the constitution of India was formed. Under an abolition, forced or bonded labour was termed as a punishable offence. The Land reform policy was the precursor to Zamindar abolition act. This ensured social justice and upliftment of peasant and farmers to a considerable extent.

Land reform is a policy that aimed at ensuring social justice and harmony. Land reform involves the changing of laws, regulations or customs regarding land ownership. Land-reform policy in India has two specific objectives :

(i) Removal of disorder and unevenness in agricultural structure that were being followed since many generations, which will eventually result in progressive increase in agricultural production.

(ii) Elimination of all elements of exploitation and social injustice within the agricultural system, to provide security for the farmer and owner of soil and assure equality of status and opportunity to all sections of the rural population.

There are four main categories of reforms:

1. **Abolition of mediators :** To minimise the wastage of profit share.
2. **Tenancy regulation :** To improve the contractual terms including security of occupancy.
3. **Ceiling on landholdings :** To redistribute surplus land to the landless.
4. Attempts to merge unequal landholdings.

Land reforms support unbiased development of all classes of people who are practicing agriculture. Unlike in pre-independence period, the ownership of the land stayed with the rich Zamindar class, they became more powerful year after year, accumulating wealth. The peasants, who actually cultivated the land, were often in poverty and remained landless. Land reforms are essential steps towards social and economic equality as land is a fundamental asset needed for healthy development of an individual.

1.4 INTEGRATED RURAL DEVELOPMENT

Rural development is the process of improving the quality of life and economic well-being of people living in rural areas, often relatively isolated and sparsely populated areas. Rural development programs many a times focuses only on economic or agricultural development. While an Integrated Rural Development focuses on scope of improvisation in all activities and needs of rural areas, ranging from education to economic development. Thus, it is a holistic approach. The objectives of Integrated Rural Development are :

1. To ensure economic stability to the rural families.
2. To increase employment opportunities in rural areas. This can be done by promoting and creating market for indigenous and exotic skills and talents like pottery, painting, sculpture, entertainment programmes (folk dance, music, plays), eco-tourism, etc.
3. To provide quality education to children.
4. To improvise medical facilities in rural areas.
5. To set-up proper transport facilities (bus, train, etc.)
6. To improvise awareness and knowledge of rural citizens regarding advancements in technology, importance of education, women empowerment, pollution, hygiene, good farming practices, etc.
7. To provide a minimum of basic facilities like electricity, water supply, telephone network connections, access to internet, etc.

Social and Community forestry : In Community forestry the local community plays a significant role in forest management and land use decision making by themselves in the facilitating support of government as well as change agents. It involves the participation and collaboration of various participants including community, government and non-government organisations-(NGOs).Social forestry is the management and protection of forest and afforestation of barren and deforested lands with the purpose of helping environmental, social and rural development. These innovative methods of forestry have lot of benefits. Involvement of local people makes such programmes successful.

The major advantages of Social and Community forestry are detailed below :

1. It boosts local economy by creating new posts and jobs.

2. It fosters a sense of responsibility, participation and unity.

3. It improves awareness and knowledge about the uses and sustainable management of forest resources. This ensures long term benefit to the local people.

4. Well maintained and sustained forestry management enhances aesthetic values of the area.

5. Threats to forests like forest fire, over – exploitation of resources are considerably reduced.

However, due to below mentioned reasons; community forestry has been a failure in many places :

(a) Community Woodlots : Develop-ment of fuel wood plantations on community wastelands was preferred, as it generates employment for the local poor and the landless.

(b) Strip Plantations : Saplings of tall growing tree species are planted along the railway tracks, canal bunds and roadsides.The landless families were involved in protecting them.

(c) Farm Forestry and decentralised nurseries : Farmers culture plantations like eucalyptus, casuarina, popular, teak, etc. on their agricultural lands.These crops are raw materials for various commercial products, which fetch lucrative price for the farmers.

(d) Lack of organisational and managerial competencies : Skills related to organising forest programmes, day-to-day decision making, marketing skills, ability to resolve internal conflicts and ensuring community benefit are often lacked in rural areas.

(e) Lack of awareness about energy conservation : Several energy conservation measures like promotion of improved wood stoves and biogas plants did not achieve the expected results due to poor publicity and awareness.

? Intext Questions

1. What is land reform?
2. List out the main categories of land reforms
3. What is Integrated Rural Development?

1.5 ROLE OF WOMEN AND COMMUNITY IN CONSERVATION

According to study conducted by the World Bank in 1991, it states that "Women play an essential role in the management of natural resources, including soil, water, forests and energy and often have a profound traditional and contemporary knowledge of the natural world around them". The importance of participation of community in conservation of environment is very evident. The holistic and sustainable development of rural areas is incomplete without the participation of community especially women. In most of the rural places, gender roles and responsibilities in domestic work, expose women more closely to resources like forests, water, land and wildlife. Ecofeminism also considers that women are closer to environment than men. This closeness, therefore, makes women more nurturing and caring towards their environment. Role of women in conserving natural resources can be briefly listed as follows :

1. Women manage natural resources daily in their roles as farmers, domestic workers and household providers. They often have unique knowledge of local crop species.

Fascinating Facts

The famous Chipko movement (Hug/stick to) of Uttarakhand in the Himalayas inspired the villagers of the Uttara Kannada district of Karnataka to initiate a similar *movement* to save their forests. The movement was called 'Appiko (hug) Movement'.

2. To meet family needs, rural women and girls walk long distances to fetch fuel, wood and water. Therefore, they are aware about availability of natural resources and are accountable for judicious use of the same.

3. Women are usually more pious and happen to worship many trees, animals, rivers or nature. Therefore, it is unlikely that they exploit the resources for their greed.

The conservation of natural resources in rural areas cannot be done without the involvement and training of women. They need to be educated on the values, management and sustainability of natural resources as alternative sources of livelihood. Involving women in protecting the environment would help societies develop the sense of responsibility needed to maintain a good balance between humans and the earth's resources. The remarkable 'Chipko Movement' initiated by a group of ladies has set an example of participation of women in conservation of environment. The Chipko Movement started in the early 20th century in the state of Uttarakhand. 84 villagers risked their lives to protect the forest trees from being felled.

1.6 COMBATING DEFORESTATION

Deforestation is the permanent destruction of forests in order to make the land available for other uses. Several million square kilometres of forest are cut down every year. The destructive effects of deforestation like loss of biodiversity, global warming, loss of resources and heritage are evident. Implementing measures to combat deforestation is the need of the hour.

Forests cover one-third of the world's land area and host more than half of the world's land-based plant and animal species.

(a) Reforestation : Reforestation is the practice of replenishing existing forests that have been depleted through deforestation.Reforestation is a very important procedure in order to save our planet. Huge forests are being destroyed or damaged due to various reasons on a daily basis. Forest fires, agricultural needs, urbanisation, logging, industrialisation and mining are some of the common factors. Reforestation ensures check on complete depletion of forests. We must ensure that a plant is planted.

(b) Energy plantation : Energy plantation refers to growing certain species of trees and shrubs which are harvestable in a comparably shorter time and are specifically meant for fuel. The fuel wood may be used either directly in wood burning stoves and boilers or processed into methanol, ethanol and producer gas. Energy plantations absorb a significant amount of carbon dioxide. The amount of carbon dioxide released while burning these wood is less compared to the fossil fuels.The consumption of trees for firewood or fuel purposes will be less if we cultivate energy plantation.

(c) Forest harvesting of non-timber forest products : Non-timber forest products (NTFPs) are preferred over timber products because, it does not involve logging of trees. (NTFPs) are biological resources other than timber that can be harvested from forest for subsistence and/or for trade. Therefore, sustained use of NTFPs is the key to sustainable forest management.

Alternatives to timber :

1. Reclaimed wood from demolished barns, old crates or barrels can be re-mould and used for making various articles.

2. Bamboo, flax, hemp and wheat straw can be used for making paper.

3. Bamboos are fast growing grass with texture of wood. It can be used to make furniture and materials.

4. Used paper should be recycled to reduce the cutting of trees to produce more paper.

5. Wood composites with recycled plastic also can be used for making several materials required in our daily life.

6. Replacing stones and metal with wood for construction purpose.

(d) Exploring alternative resources for livelihood : We depend on forest resources especially trees for various day to day needs. Deforestation is being done for satisfying our needs for energy, food and various day to day usage products like furniture, paper, medicines, etc..It is essential to explore and use alternative resources. Renewable sources of energy like solar, hydropower, geothermal, wind energy, etc are clean sources of energy. Using renewable sources of energy not only reduces the need to cut trees for food, but also contributes in controlling pollution and other ill-effects on environment. Wood is used on a large scale for making furniture, paper and in construction. Using alternatives for wood in these sectors is also important. Furniture can be made up of bamboo, fibre, plastic, metals, etc. Paper can be made from sugarcane residue and bamboo, which is a substitute for wood. Recycling used and waste paper should be encouraged to reduce felling of trees.

(e) Change in consumption patterns : Sustained consumption and use of resources is the key to conservation of resources. Consumption patterns must change to combat deforestation. All citizens and industries must be encouraged to follow the 3R principle. Reducing the consumption, reusing the product by making necessary modifications and recycling products wherever possible is the best way to minimise waste and resource exploitation. Capping over consumption of forest resources to manufacture various products should be levied. Over production always leads to un-sustained methods of marketing and selling goods. Such marketing schemes invite more demand for the products, which fosters speedy forest depletion.

1.7 MANAGING FOREST GRAZING

Forest areas make up a significant portion of lands used for livestock grazing. Livestock owners depend on forest land for various reasons. The causes of forest grazing are as follows :

(i) Improper land use : Pasture lands is a basic requirement in an area with live stocks. In most of the rural areas this basic requirement is ignored, maybe because they have an easy access to the forest. The zoning and planning of land is not effectively done.

(ii) Overstocking : Overstocking implies a situation where a piece of land is intensively stocked with more animals than the site can support for a grazing season. In the majority of the cases, animals are more than the average land available for grazing. Therefore, livestock owners immensely exploit the forest plants and trees.

(iii) Drought or poor irrigation methods : Pasture lands should be maintained by providing adequate water supply. If the area faces drought condition or does not have efficient irrigation facilities, then growth of foliage is difficult.

The consequences of forest grazing are as follows :

1. **Soil erosion :** Overgrazing leads to soil erosion. The nutritious top soil is washed away, making the soil less nutritious.

2. **Soil degradation :** Soil erosion leads to depletion of soil quality. The fertility of soil is affected.

3. **Loss of species :** Overgrazing leads to speedy depletion of forest plants. The time taken to replenish theses plants is much slower than the depletion speed. The microbes, forest animals or insects dependant on such plant will be affected.

4. **Imbalance in forest ecosystem :** Overgrazing leads to depletion of forest plants which eventually affects the forest food chain and food web. Thus, the forest ecosystem is disturbed.

In 1988, Government of India articulated a National Forest Policy with an objective to conserve forest areas. It aimed at conserving forest areas by maintaining environmental stability, checking soil erosion, introducing practices for the use of forest resources in a sustained manner, afforestation, creating awareness among people and involving people in forestry management. One of clauses of this policy also focused on controlling forest grazing. Special conservation areas were identified and young plantations and regeneration areas were fully protected. The need to control grazing and browsing in forest was mentioned.

The clause also specifies levying adequate grazing fees to discourage people in forest areas from maintaining large herds of non-essential livestock. The objectives of National Forest Policy, 1988 are as follows –

1. Maintenance of environmental stability through preservation and restoration of the ecological balance that has been adversely disturbed by serious depletion of the forests of the country.

2. Conserving the natural heritage of the country by preserving the remaining natural forests with the vast variety of flora and fauna.

3. Checking soil erosion in the catchment areas of rivers, lakes, reservoirs in the interest of soil and water conservation.

4. Taking appropriate measures for mitigating floods and droughts and for the retardation of siltation of reservoirs.

5. Checking the extension of sand-dunes in the desert areas of Rajasthan and along the coastal tracts.

6. Increasing substantially the forest or tree cover in the country through massive afforestation and social forestry programmes, especially on all denuded, degraded and unproductive lands.

7. Meeting the requirements of fuelwood, fodder, minor forest produce and small timber of the rural and tribal populations.

8. Increasing the productivity of forests to meet essential national needs.

9. Encouraging efficient utilisation of forest produce and maximising substitution of wood.

10. Creating a massive people's movement with the involvement of women, for achieving these objectives and to minimise pressure on existing forests.

SUMMARY

- Soil degradation can be defined as a process by which one or more of the potential ecological functions of the soil are harmed.
- Soil erosion is the displacement of the upper layer of soil. The agents of soil erosion are water and wind.
- Human activities like use of chemical pesticides, unsustainable agricultural practices, excessive farming, water pollution and land pollution have resulted in soil degradation.
- Soil conservation is the practice of protecting the soil against erosion or deterioration.
- Land reform involves the changing of laws, regulations or customs regarding land ownership.
- In social and community forestry, local people play a significant role in forest management and land use decision making.
- Forest grazing has various ill impacts on environment.

EXERCISE

A. Define each of these terms :

1. Soil erosion
2. Ploughing
3. Dry farming
4. Deforestation
5. Reforestation

B. Answer the following in brief :

1. Soil profile can be enhanced by practicing various cropping systems. Justify the statement.

2. What are the objectives of land-reform policy?
3. Write any two causes of forest grazing.

C. Answer the following in detail :

1. Explain the mechanical practices of soil conservation.
2. What are the objectives of Integrated Rural development?
3. How can we conserve soil and water together?
4. Enlist some alternatives to timber.
5. Explain the objectives and clauses of National Forest Policy?

D. Previous Years Boards questions :

1. Give two vegetative means of soil conservation.
2. Give two advantages of conservation tillage.
3. What is soil erosion? Explain the direct and indirect effects of soil erosion.
4. Define Global Environment Health.
5. What are the reasons for the failure of Community Forests Project?
6. Explain the role of women in conservation of forest. Illustrate your answer with an example.
7. Write two advantages of growing big trees along the roadside.
8. Overgrazing is a menace. Give three impacts of overgrazing and two methods to control the menace.

WORKSHEET

A. Fill in the blanks :

1. The method of farming without irrigation is called ______.
2. ______ occurs when water is channelled across unprotected land and washes away the soil along the drainage lines.
3. In _______ a number of small water reservoirs are made along the contour.
4. In India, prior to independence, the _____ preserved the rights to collect tax on the behalf of king.

B. Write two advantages of the following :

1. Use of organic manure
2. Community forestry
3. Dry farming
4. National Forest Policy 1988

C. Read the following excerpts and answer the questions that follow. (open-ended questions) :

1. Melghat is a forest in the state of Maharashtra. It is being observed that many livestock owners from the nearby villages take their cattle and goat for grazing to this forest.

(a) What could be the probable reasons for the forest grazing?

2. Ram owns a paper industry. He gets the raw material *i.e.*, timber from the nearby forests. But, the government has now levied a restriction on cutting the trees for commercial purposes.

(a) Suggest the alternative ways of producing paper from non-timber resources.

D. Activities :

1. Research and prepare a report on various policies by made Government of India to promote rural development.

5 FOOD

1.0 INTRODUCTION

Food is one of the basic needs of man. Food contains the nutrition that we need to remain healthy. The major nutrients supplied by food include carbohydrates, proteins, vitamins, minerals and fat. Food can be obtained from plant sources as well as animal source. Thousands of species of plants and animals are harvested for food. Some species of fungi (mushrooms) and bacteria are also edible. In olden days, man used to obtain food by hunting or agriculture. But, today, majority of the food comes from the food industry. Dynamic changes have occurred in food production practices in the 20th century. Industrialisation and development in science and technology are two reasons for such a progress. World agriculture produces enough food calories to meet the energy needs of the current population which is approximately 6 billion. But the growing population will demand for more food resources, which may one day lead to food shortage. In addition to population explosion, issues like pollution, urbanisation, deforestation, etc. are contributing to problems like scarcity of resources for agriculture (land, water), poor quality or distorted crops (due to polluted soil and water), etc. In order to increase the yield, we have been implementing various practices like clearing up forest areas for growing food crops, using chemicals in the form of fertilizers, pesticides and insecticides, faulty irrigation practices which have led to ecological imbalance. Soil degradation, soil erosion, loss of diversity, exhaustion of resources, pollution are some of the effects on environment caused due to faulty practices. Efforts to meet the food demands has to be made by considering environmental impacts also.

1.1 SUSTAINABLE AGRICULTURE

Agriculture has changed dramatically, especially since the end of World War–II. Food and productivity ascended due to new technologies, mechanisation and increased chemical use. Government policies also favoured maximising production. These changes allowed farmers with reduced labour demands to produce more food. However, significant ill-effects are also evident. Topsoil depletion, groundwater contamination, the decline of family farms, increasing costs of production, and the disintegration of economic and social conditions in rural communities are some of prominent effects.

Sustainable agriculture is a farming practice which incorporates sustainable practices by considering ecosystem services. The term 'sustainable agriculture' was first coined by Australian agricultural scientist Gordon McClymond. The goal of sustainable agriculture is to meet society's food needs in the present without compromising the ability of future generations to meet their needs. Sustainable agriculture cares about a healthy environment, economic profitability, and social and economic equity. Every person involved in the food system–growers, food processors, distributors, retailers, consumers and waste managers can play a role in ensuring a sustainable agricultural system.

> **Fascinating Fact**
>
> Globally, agriculture water withdrawals (2,703 km^3/yr) account for more than double the combined withdrawals for municipal and industrial use (468 km^3/yr and 731 km^3/yr, respectively), out of which 15-35% is estimated to be unsustainable.

Following are the best practices of sustainable agriculture.

(i) Integrated Pest Management (IPM) : When modern pesticides were first developed, they were used extensively. Pests susceptible to a pesticide were quickly killed, leaving resistant ones to breed and multiply. Overuse of pesticides caused the development of resistant pests. Scientists developed a new approach to pest control, which was Integrated Pest Management (IPM). IPM includes all the pest control techniques by integrating appropriate measures that discourage the development of pest populations and keep pesticides and other interventions to levels that are economically justified and reduce or minimize risks to human health and the environment.

The objectives of IPM are as follows :

(a) To keep the pest numbers below Economic Threshold Level (ETL) instead of their eradication.

(b) To protect and conserve the environ-ment including biodiversity.

(c) To make plant protection feasible, safe and economical for the farmers.

(d) To ensure that harvests are sufficient and of good enough quality to adequately nourish the farmer's families and other consumers who depend on them.

The IPM approach

A careful evaluation of each pest infestation is the first step of IPM. The life cycle of the pest, nature of the damage caused by the pest, predators, effects of weather and other such factors are considered before a control plan is implemented. For example, weeds like Queen Anne's lace (*Daucus carota*) can dwell beneficial insects such as lacewing or lady beetle larvae that help keep aphid and other pest populations at tolerable levels. Clover growing in a lawn may be viewed as an unwanted weed, but as a legume it is synthesizing nitrogen for the soil and the flowers are providing nectar to honey bees and other pollinators. Therefore, tolerance for some weeds may be part of an IPM plan. A woodpecker makes holes in the trunk of a peach tree, but at the same time it feeds on the insect larvae that may cause more damage to the tree.

IPM is an integral component of crop management which looks at all aspects necessary to grow a crop. The control options are usually a combination of physical, biological and chemical aspects to manage crops, pests and diseases.

Advantages of Integrated Pest Management :

Besides lowering the effects of chemicals in the ecosystem and food chain, there are several other advantages of IPM, which are listed as follows :

(a) Slower development of resistance to pesticides : Pests have a tendency to develop a resistance to pesticides over time. The pests that survive the application of the chemicals will pass on their genes to their offspring. This leads to the creation of "super-pests". IPM reduces the risks and chances of these phenomenon.

(b) Maintaining a balanced ecosystem : The use of pesticides may eradicate the pest population along with the non-targeted organisms. Over application of pesticides usually results in depletion of useful bacteria present in the soil. IPM maintains the balance of the ecosystem.

(c) Reduced risk to farm workers : Farmers and their families suffer various health issues (respiratory problems, skin infection, etc.) due to over exposure to the harmful chemicals present in the pesticides. IPM reduces health risks to farmers and their families.

(d) Reduced chemical and labour costs : The reduced usage of pesticides is more cost effective in the long term.

(e) Better crop quality : When a pesticide is applied to crops, the constituent chemicals of the pesticide enter the food chain when consumer eats it. This is called as biomagnification. Biomagnification is the increase in concentration of a substance, such as a toxic chemical, in the tissues of organisms at successively higher levels in a food chain. The restricted use of such chemicals in IPM approach, reduces the chances of such contaminations. This boosts consumer confidence and satisfaction.

Disadvantages of Integrated Pest Management (IPM)

Though IPM aims at producing good quality crops by implementing vivid measures, it does have a few demerits. Following are the disadvantages of IPM :

(a) **Involvement of lot of technicalities :** IPM involves in detail and minute study of crop species, pest species, life cycle of pests, nature of damage they cause to the crops, their role in ecosystem and selection of mode of pest management. Different pests have different control methods, and it is necessary to monitor which methods are the best for specific pests. Each farmer and all those involved in IPM have to be educated and trained about all these aspects, which could be difficult sometimes.

(b) **Time consuming :** Application of IPM requires close monitoring. IPM does not give fast results when compared to the pesticides.

(c) **Resource requirement :** IPM requires more resources which are appropriate to the nature of pests as well as crops.

? Intext Questions

1. Define sustainable agriculture.
2. what is the goal of sustainable agricuture?
3. What is biomagnification ?

(ii) Genetically Modified Organisms (GMO)

Humans have been making genetic modifications in domesticated plants and animals since centuries ago, through selective breeding or artificial selection. These were artificial method by opposing natural selection. Selective breeding was carried out to obtain desired traits in domesticated plants and animals. But the technology has progressed much ahead, where we are able to alter DNA and produce genetically modified organism. A genetically modified organism (GMO) is any organism whose genetic material has been altered using genetic engineering techniques. A GMO (genetically modified organism) is the result of a laboratory process where genes from the DNA of one species are extracted and artificially forced into the genes of an unrelated plant or animal. The foreign genes may come from bacteria, viruses, insects, animals or even humans. This technology finds its application in food industry, where many plants, animals and strains of microbes have been genetically modified.

(A) Genetically modified plants : Plants with favourable characteristics have been produced for thousands of years by traditional breeding methods. Desirable traits are selected, combined and propagated by repeated sexual crossings over numerous generations. This process takes about 15 years to produce new varieties. Genetic engineering can produce plants with favourable characteristics in a very short span of duration.

(1) Transgenic plants : Transgenic plants are produced by the movement or insertion of a gene into a plant that normally does not have a copy of that gene.

Bt cotton is an example of transgenic plant. Bt cotton varieties are incorporated with a gene from a bacterium (*Bacillus thuringiensis*). *Bacillus thuringiensis* is found in the soil that causes the transgenic cotton to produce an insecticidal protein. The protein thus produced destroys the plant eating pests and insects.Another example of transgenic plant is tobacco plant incorporated with certain DNA. A nematode *Meloidegyneincognitia* infects the roots of tobacco plants and causes a great reduction in yield. A nematode specific DNA was introduced into the host tobacco plant. The introduction of such a DNA in the host plant prevented further translation of RNA into protein. Thus, the parasite cannot survive in the host.The transgenic plant therefore got itself protected from the parasite.

(2) Genetically modified crops : The DNA of plants are modified to adapt or survive in certain conditions. DNA modifications are also done in order to enhance their productivity or qualities. The plants produced or modified in such a way are called as Genetically modified crops. The aim of this technology is to inculcate a trait in the plant which does not naturally occur. Some of desired traits in crops are resistance to certain pests, diseases, chemical treatments or environmental conditions, reduction of spoilage or improving the nutrient profile of the crop which can be achieved by genetically modifying the crops. A remarkable example of genetically modified crops is golden rice. Golden rice is a species of rice produced through genetic engineering. This strain of rice was incorporated with DNA to synthesise beta-carotene. Beta-carotene is a precursor of vitamin A. The genetic modification of rice was done to combat the shortage of dietary vitamin A. Rice was fortified with vitamin A, as it is the staple food for people in Asian countries, making it the perfect crop for targeting vitamin deficiencies.

Fascinating Fact

Recently, scientists have developed tomatoes that resist frost and freezing temperatures by the virtue of anti-freeze genes which are extracted from a cold-water fish, the winter flounder (*Pseudopleuronectes americanus*).

(B) Genetically modified animals : Genetically modified animals are the animals that contain additional or altered genetic material through the use of modern biotechnology tools. The intention behind such modification is to give the animal a new trait or characteristic. Plenty of livestock animals have been genetically engineered to empower with valuable traits in terms of nutritive value, disease resistance, life span and reproduction. For example, pigs have been genetically engineered to incorporate the omega–12 fatty acid desaturase gene which is responsible for higher levels of omega-3. Inclusion of omega–3 in our diet is very beneficial as it reduces the risk factors for heart diseases, blood pressure and high cholesterol. Cattle have been genetically engineered to produce an enzyme, which makes it to produce the milk containing lactoferrin. Lactoferrin boosts the immunity in human infants. Goats have been genetically engineered to produce milk with improved quality and quantity of proteins in their milk. Such advances may add to the nutritional value of animal-based products.

Fascinating Fact

The Liger is a crossbred of a female tiger and a male lion. They possess characteristics from both parents, for example, their social behaviour from lions and the swimming ability from tigers.

ILL effects of Genetic engineering on environment :

(a) The creation of new genetic species could cause an imbalance in the ecology.

(b) An accident in engineering the genetics of a virus or bacteria could result in a stronger or predator organism, which could cause a serious epidemic when released.

(c) Some GMOs can be toxic to non-target organisms.

(d) GMOs put biodiversity at risk. Usually, GMOs are planted in a monocrop way, therefore, most of the heritage plants and trees are diminished.

(e) The DNA of GMO gets involved in the food chain and food pyramid. GMO's DNA may end up mingling in the soil, compost, animal feed and by-products.

Intext Questions

1. How are GMOs artificially made?
2. What are transgenic plants?
3. How do GMOs put biodiversity at risk?

(C) New crop strain : In biology, a strain is a low-level taxonomic rank of plant, animal or microorganism.Developing new strains through methods like hybridisation, is one of methods to increase crop yield.

(1) High yielding crop varieties : Seed is elementary to crop production and thus to the food security and rural development also. The sustainable availability of good-quality seed is therefore an important development issue. Emerging trends in seed industries have made a range of options available to the farmer, cultivator or agriculturist. High yielding varieties are one such option. High-yielding varieties (HYVs) are developed by scientists to improve food supplies. HYVagricultural crops are characterized by the following traits :

1. Higher crop yield per area (hectare)
2. Dwarfness
3. Improved response to fertilizers
4. High reliance on irrigation and fertilizers
5. Early maturation

Most common HYVs can be found among wheat, corn, soybean, rice, potato and cotton. A remarkable example of HYV is varieties of rice called BR–11 dhan-33 and BINA dhan-7 which was developed by scientists. These varieties of rice mature in less than four months; therefore, they are suited for famine conditions.

The advantages of High Yielding Variety seeds over Traditional Varieties of Seeds are as follows :

1. The duration of maturation of HYV crops is less compared to the traditional varieties of seeds. Therefore, farmers can opt for multiple cropping.

2. HYV crops are more productive than the traditional varieties of seeds. The per capita yield of HYV crops is much higher than the usual seeds. Therefore, these seeds are a better option for producing surplus yield.

3. The HYV crops are usually short. Their short stature enables them to withstand the strong wind.

4. The HYV crops respond better to fertilizers and pesticides compared to the usual crops.Therefore, when fertilizers are supplied to high yielding varieties their yield increases substantially.

However, these HYV show some undesirable qualities and drawbacks too. They are :

1. HYVs demand ample amount of resources in the form of irrigation (water) and nutrients (fertilizers). Thereby, increasing the cost to the farmers.

2. HYVs are more sensitive to diseases and pests. Therefore, they need more pesticides and maintenance compared to the traditional varieties of seeds.

3. HYVs also need constant and regular weeding.

4. HYV seeds are costlier than the usual forms.

(2) Hybrid Varieties : A hybrid or a crossbreed is the result of combining the qualities of two organisms of different breeds, varieties, species or genera through sexual reproduction. As a result of breeding, plants with desirable traits which are naturally not found in their parent population are produced. Hybrid seeds are widely used in agriculture and gardening. Hybrid seeds are one of major contributors to dramatic increase in agricultural yield. IR8, Jaya, Jyoti and Awasti are some examples of hybrid rice. High resistance from pests and diseases, high yield, high productivity and more life span are some of the improved characteristics of hybrid plants.

Even though hybrid seeds exhibit these improvised features, it has a few limitations :

1. Hybrid seeds perform well in terms of yield during its first life cycle. However, the yield drops if they are recycled for the next lifecycle. This becomes a big disadvantage for the poor farmers, when they have to purchase hybrid seeds every year.

2. Hybridisation limits the chances of evolution, as we focus and promote the growth of certain type of species with required traits.
3. The hybrid strains consume more resources in terms of water, nutrients and soil. This leads to exhaustion in that place causing scarcity of resources.

(d) Cropping patterns

(1) Mixed cropping : It is a type of agriculture that involves planting two or more plants simultaneously in the same field, so that they grow together. Mixed cropping is also known as polyculture, inter-cropping, or co-cultivation. However, care should be taken while choosing the combination of crops to be planted in the same field. They should have same nutrient requirement, otherwise all species will compete with each other for nutrients. As a result, growth and yield will be poor. Some common combinations of mixed cropping methods are - wheat + gram, wheat + mustard, groundnut + sunflower.

The three sisters : A classic example of mixed cropping

The well-known example of mixed cropping is that of the American "three sisters": maize, beans and cucurbits (squash and pumpkins). The Seneca and Iroquois tribes in the US northeast sometime in 1000 CE practiced mixed cropping. The method consists of planting all three seeds in the same hole. As they grow, the maize provides a stalk for the beans to climb on, the beans are nutrient-rich to offset that taken out by the maize, and the squash grows low to the ground to keep weeds down and keep water from evapourating from the soil in the heat.

The **intercropping system** also follows the similar theory, but with a small difference. Intercropping is growing two or more crops simultaneously on the same field in a definite pattern. A few rows of one crop alternate with a few rows of a second crop, for example, soyabean + maize, or finger millet (bajra) + cowpea (lobia). The differences between the mixed cropping system and the intercropping system are listed below :

Mixed Cropping	Intercropping
Crops are either sown in rows or mixed without considering the population of strains of crops taken.	Crops are sown in different rows without affecting the population of main crop when sown as sole crop.
All crops are considered equal.	More emphasis is given to the main crop.
The main objective is to get at least one crop under favourable conditions.	The main object is to utilise the space left between two rows of main crop.

Advantages of Mixed Cropping :

1. The field space is well utilised as the farmers can keep their fields under continuous production.

2. If planned properly, amount of artificial fertilizer can be reduced.

3. Due to geographic mixing of crops the spread of pest and other diseases may slow down.

4. Availability of land to be farmed is more with the same amount of labour and machinery.

5. There is increase in the yield in mixed farming when compared to the monoculture.

Disadvantages of Mixed Cropping :

1. It is difficult to find the right combination of crops. All crops cannot be grown in mixed farming practices.

2. Crops for mixed farming if not chosen properly, have chances of competition between the crops for nutrients.

3. Each crop has different nutrient requirement; thus, it may reduce the fertility of the soil as more than one crop are grown at a time in the same piece of land.

(2) Regenerative farming practices : Soil being an important resource for agriculture, it is crucial to find ways to regenerate and rejuvenate the agricultural land to facilitate growth of crops. In every stage of agriculture, the financial, social and environmental aspects should be considered. Regenerative agriculture is an approach to food and farming systems that regenerates topsoil and increases biodiversity. This approach also aims to capture the carbon in the soil and above ground biomass, which reverses the effect of atmospheric accumulation. It involves holistic implementation and management of organic farming, agroecology and agroforestry.

The four principles of the regenerative farming are :

1. Progressively–improve whole agroecosystems (soil, water and biodiversity).

2. Create context-specific designs and make holistic decisions that express the essence of each farm.

3. Ensure and develop just and reciprocal relationships amongst all stakeholders.

4. Continually grow and evolve individuals, farms and communities to express their innate potential.

(i) Crop rotation : The method of growing of different crops on a piece of land in a sequence is known as crop rotation. The maturation time of the crops, availability of moisture and irrigation facilities decide the choice of the crop to be cultivated after one harvest. If crop rotation is done properly then two or three crops can be grown in a year with good harvests. It is done so that the soil of farms is not used for only one set of nutrients. It helps in reducing soil erosion and increases soil fertility and crop yield. In addition, crop rotation mitigates the build-up of pathogens and pests which further becomes indigenous. The soil structure and fertility also increases due to biomass from varied root structures. The choice of crops depends on the goals of the cultivator or farmer. These purposes are classified as follows :

(a) Row crops : These are commercially valued crops like vegetables. Row crops have small roots and low biomass. Row crops fail to counter or mitigate soil depletion.

(b) Legumes : Legumes like clover, groundnuts, etc. fix atmospheric nitrogen in their root nodules in the form of nitrates and nitrites. When these plants are harvested, the biomass of unharvested roots impart nitrogenous compounds to the soil. Nitrogenous nutrients are very essential to the plant growth.

(c) Grasses and cereals : These plants usually play the role of cover crops. Their dense fibrous root system provides a good structure to the soil. It also mitigates soil erosion.

Fascinating Fact

In developing children, pesticide exposure contributes to neurological problems, which impair learning, memory and attention.

(ii) Agroforestry : Agroforestry is a land use management system in which trees or shrubs are grown around or among crops or pastureland. It combines shrubs and trees in agricultural and forestry technologies to create more diverse, productive, profitable, healthy, ecologically sound and sustainable land-use systems. Agroforestry systems include both traditional and modern land-use systems where trees are managed together with crops and animal production systems in agricultural settings. They are dynamic, ecologically based, natural resource management systems that diversify and sustain production in order to increase social, economic and environmental benefits for land users at all scales. There are two main types of agroforestry :

(a) Agri-silvicultural systems : These are a combination of crops and trees. This system is common in all agro-ecological zones of Nepal, where agriculture crops are grown in terrace flat and trees are grown in terrace bunds, borders and slopes.

(b) Silvopastural systems : These combine forestry and grazing of domesticated animals on pastures, rangelands or on-farm.In the UK, there is a nationwide experiment called The Silvopastural National Network Experiment in which a number of tree species and planting densities are being studied over a range of sites.

(c) Polyvarietal cultivation : It is a method of planting of a plot of land with the crops with the several varieties of the same crops. It is similar to intercropping or mixed-cropping where two or more types of crops are cultivated on the same land at the same time. This method aims at effective utilisation of resources, increase in yield and resistance against weather conditions, diseases and pests. When compared with intercropping or mixed cropping methods, this method has an additional advantage. There is less competition for nutrients as the crops grown are of same species.

(d) Polyculture : It is practice of growing multiple crops in one farming place. It is a complex form of intercropping which involves practices such as multiple cropping, companion planting and agroforestry. A research showed that if numerous varieties of rice are planted in the same field, the yields increases considerably. Resistance from diseases and pests is the main reason for increase in yield. Thus, it can be said that polyculture enhances immunity. Crop diversity also improves in this practice. If cultivated properly, such farms can provide food, fuel and fertilizers and also meet other food needs of farmers. When different types of plantation are done on the land, root systems of different plants reach different depths in the soil and capture nutrients and moisture efficiently and minimize the need for fertilizer and irrigation. The field is always covered by the crops or plants; thus the soil erosion is significantly controlled.

? Intext Questions

1. What are High Yielding Varieties?
2. What is the difference between agrisilvicultural systems and silvopastural system?
3. How does crop rotation help in pest control?

(e) Tillage : Tillage or field ploughing is a very important step in agriculture. It is the process of preparation of soil by various methods like digging, stirring or over turning. The soil is made loose during ploughing for plant to grow. The roots of the soil can penetrate through loose soil easily. The seepage of water and nutrients also becomes easier in the loose soil. However, if the ploughed field is left uncovered or unused for a long time, the land becomes susceptible to soil erosion and degradation.

(1) Conservation tillage : Conservation tillage is the method of tillage that leaves the previous year's crop residue on fields before and after planting the next crop, to reduce soil erosion and runoff. The presence of residue slows down the speed of flowing water. Conservation tillage can be done in following ways :

1. **No tillage :** This method aims at 100% retention of residues.

2. Strip tillage : In this method, the field is ploughed in strips. The seeds are sowed in the tilled portion of the field. The in between soil the strips are left unploughed.

3. Mulch tillage : In this method atleast one-third of the harvest residue is left in the field. If the residue is left on the field, the speed of flow of water is cut due to irregular surface.

4. Ridge tillage : This method involves planting crops on permanent ridges which are usually about 4-6 inches high.

5. Rotational tillage : In this method, this tillage activity is planned and carried periodically, maybe after 2 years or 3 years according to the soil texture.

Advantage of conservation tillage :

1. Reduces soil erosion as the field is not left uncovered.
2. Improves soil and water quality by adding organic matter as crop residue decomposes; this creates an open soil structure that lets water in more easily, reducing runoff.
3. Conserves water by reducing evaporation at the soil surface.
4. Conserves energy, time, fuel and money due to fewer trips across the field. The cost of labour and machinery is also lessened.
5. Reduces potential air pollution from dust and diesel emissions.
6. Crop residue provides food and cover for wildlife.
7. Improves soil moisture by enhancing crop growth in dry periods or on droughty soils

Conservation tillage has a few drawbacks too. Those are :

1. Conservation tillage requires strategic planning before the execution.
2. The tillage should be maintained. For example, in a strip tillage method, the field is ploughed in strips pattern. However, the ploughed strips have to be maintained or else the ploughed area will get covered due the blowing wind or flowing water.

(f) Irrigation : Irrigation is the artificial application of water to soil, in the correct amounts and frequency, for optimal soil infiltration and plant growth. Water is an irreplaceable requisite for the plant growth. It is not possible to always depend on rain water. Crops grow well when proper quality and quantity of water supply is done. Crops have specific water requirements which vary according to the climatic condition, species, structure and mass of the plant. The minerals and nutrients in the soil dissolve in water, absorbed by the roots and raise to the shoot of the plants. It is very important to select proper method of irrigation. Faulty irrigation practices will not only damage the plant but also cause soil erosion. Ineffective and unplanned irrigation is one of the major reasons for wastage of water.

(1) Drip irrigation or trickle drip irrigation

In this method water drips in to soil at very low rates from a network of pipes fitted with outlets or holes called emitters or drippers. In drip irrigation, plants are watered in such a way that only the part of soil in which roots are anchored is wetted. Drip irrigation is apt for the crops which are grown in rows and contours. Mainline pipe, sub-line pipe, drippers, filters, valves and pressure regulators are the components of drip irrigation system. Each component is important for the smooth functioning of the drip irrigation system.

1. Mainline pipe and sub-line pipes are the channels through which the water flows.

2. Drippers or emitters are like small holes through which water is discharged into the soil.

3. Filters are the components which prevent clogging in the pipeline and drippers. Fine particles like sand, humus, debris, etc. are screened and prevented from entering the water channel in the pipelines.

4. Valves are installed to control the flow of water through particular pipelines.

5. Pressure regulators control the water pressure of the drip system.

There are various benefits of installing drip irrigation system but, a few shortcomings are also observed. These are enlisted below :

Advantages of drip irrigation system are :

1. This system is very effective in minimising and mitigating soil erosion and degradation.

2. It almost suits all types of soil.

3. Water distribution to all crops is uniform.

4. Sufficient amount of water is used. Drip irrigation does not give scope to water wastage.

5. Recycled waste water can be also used in the drip irrigation system.

6. Weed growth is lessened as extra water does not accumulate on the soil.

7. Roots are adequately moisturised which gives adequate time for absorption and translocation.

8. Labour cost is less than other irrigation methods.

9. The volume of water evaporating from the surface is not as much due to lesser accumulation of water on the surface of soil.

Disadvantages of drip irrigation system are :

1. Initial cost for installing drip irrigation components is more than the conventional irrigation system.

2. Pipelines and valves of drip irrigation are usually made up of plastic. These components may damage due to the continuous exposure to the heat of the sun.

3. The components need maintenance. The filters should be regularly checked for accumulation of substances. If the filters are clogged, the water supply will not be proper.

(g) Integrated Nutrient Supply Programme : Integrated Nutrient Management refers to the maintenance of soil fertility and of plant nutrient supply at an optimum level for sustaining the desired productivity through optimization of the benefits from all possible sources of organic, inorganic and biological components in an integrated manner. The aim of integrated nutrient management is to integrate the use of natural and man-made soil nutrients to increase crop productivity and preserve soil productivity for future generations. Organic fertilizers, manures, green manure, bio-fertilizers, legumes and sewage sludge are the main components of integrated nutrient management.

1. Organic fertilizers

Organic fertilizers or manures are the fertilizers derived from the decomposed animal and plant matter. Organic fertilizers are made of decomposed animal body, plant body, animal excreta, human excreta, plant waste and other biodegradable waste. They release nutrients after their decomposition. Manures contain plant nutrients in complex organic forms. Fertilizers contain naturally occurring or synthetic chemicals containing plant nutrients.Overuse of fertilizers can lead to soil pollution, soil degradation and disturbed soil ecosystem.

2. Bulky organic manures

Bulky organic manures contain small percentage of nutrients and are applied in large quantities. Farmyard manure, compost and green-manure are most widely used bulky organic manures. Farmyard manure refers to the decomposed mixture of dung and urine of farm animals along with the litter and left-over material from roughages or fodder fed the cattle. Compost is organic matter that has been decomposed and recycled to fertilize the soil. Majority of the wet waste like kitchen waste and other domestic waste can be made into a compost. Worms like earthworms, white worms and red wigglers can be used to hasten the process of composting. This is called as vermicompost.

3. Green manure

Green manure is the undecomposed plant material which is used for fertilizing the soil.It is obtained in two ways: by growing green manure crops or by collecting green leaf from plants grown in wastelands, field bunds and forest. The plants that are grown for green manure are known as green manure crops. The most important green manure crops are sunnhemp, dhaincha, pillipesara,clusterbeans and sesbaniarostrate. Green manure is broken down into plant nutrients by bacteria that consumes organic matter. Warmth and moisture fasten the process of decomposition. The plant matter releases large amounts of carbon dioxide and other macronutrients and micronutrients. Green manure gives rise to humus which makes the soil slightly acidic. Therefore, green manure can be added to the alkaline soil to neutralise it. Legumes are also a part of green manure. Legumes have nitrogen fixing bacteria in their root nodules. These bacteria fix atmospheric nitrogen into nitrates and nitrites which is passed on to the soil. Nitrogen is one of the essential nutrients for plants.

4. Biofertilizer

A biofertilizer is a substance which contains microorganisms like bacteria, algae and fungi alone or in combination which may help in increasing crop productivity. These microbes undergo certain biological processes like nitrogen fixation, solubilising phosphorus and by synthesising growth-promoting substances. Biofertilizers are either applied to the plant body or to the soil.

5. Sewage sludge

The wastewater is collected from various domestic and industrial sources. The collected wastewater is treated before letting it out to the sewage. Sewage sludge and the effluent are the two components of treated wastewater. The sludge is further dried and applied to agricultural cropland as fertilizer or made into biosolid compost for fertilizing the soil. However, sewage sludge is said to contain considerable amounts of harmful substances like hydrocarbons, heavy metals, dioxins, aromatic compounds, etc. Some of these chemicals may get absorbed by the plants and these chemicals gets incorporated in the food chain. Identifying the chemicals and understanding their pathway through all the levels of food chain and food web is a difficult task. However, it is possible to filter and treat the sewage sludge before applying to the agricultural land. But, this option may cost a lot of money, therefore it is not very feasible.

6. Gene banks

Gene banks are reservoirs or store houses which preserve genetic materials of useful plants, animals and microbe species under suitable conditions. Conserving the genetic diversity of our crops and related wild species is essential to ensure availability of these variations to future plant breeders. Such a conservation becomes vital when we consider increased food demand by a growing world population, environment degradation and climate change. Gene banks are a form of ex-situ biodiversity conservation. The gene banks are of three types :

(i) Seed bank preserves dry seeds and spores at a very low temperature.

(ii) Tissue bank is used to preserve seedless plants and plants that reproduce sexually. Meristematic tissues are stored in certain conditions and nutrient medium.

(iii) Cryobank is used to store seed or embryo at a very low temperature. Usually liquid nitrogen is used to create a temperature of –198°C.

The objectives of gene banks are mentioned below :

(a) To preserve genetic diversity.

(b) To make genetic materials available for future use in research, creating GMOs and plant breeding.

(c) To conserve species from going extinct.

1.2 PROBLEMS OF GLOBAL FOOD SECURITY, FOOD AID

The World Food Summit of 1996 defined food security as existing "when all people at all times have access to sufficient, safe, nutritious food to maintain a healthy and active life". Population explosion, climate change, depletion of natural resources and imbalance in food distribution are major causes which affect food security. The United Nations Food and Agriculture Organisation estimates that about 795 million people of the 7.3 billion people in the world, were suffering from chronic undernourishment in 2014-2016. Out of 795 million,a big majority of around 780 million people population is from developing and underdeveloped countries.This clearly depicts imbalance in food distribution or supply. Malnutrition and undernutrition is generally caused by poverty. Markets in the developed countries are often big and produce adequate amounts of food for their population to consume. In addition, factors like unemployment, food shortage, bad hygiene, lack of infrastructure, lack of technology, lack of capital, low income, unsuccessful agriculture, etc. are prominent in developing and underdeveloped nations. Such factors are responsible for creating gap and disparity in food distribution. It would be ironical to observe that as millions are not provided with adequate amounts of food while others have so much that obesity becomes an issue. Around 1.02 billion people are suffering from chronic hunger, while obesity rates are constantly rising in developed countries. Food security is an assembly of food availability, food access and food use. Food inequality results from imbalance of any of these three components. Food security is dependent on ensuring that all groups of people are fed adequately. The world produces enough food to feed everyone, however due to inefficient economic systems certain countries consume more, while deprived nations have very little chance of gaining as much resources. In order to make a difference to food insecurity the way the global economies work should change. Food aid is one of the ways to stabilise the food security. Food aid refers to the provision of food or cash to purchase food in times of emergency or to provide longer-term solutions in areas where food shortages exist. Food aid is of three types :

Fascinating Fact

Organic food is typically more expensive than conventional food, sometimes 50% higher than the same conventionally grown food.

(i) Program Food Aid : It is a form of aid where food is grown in the donor country for distribution. It is not given free of cost but, recipient countries purchase the food for lower rates.

(ii) Relief or Emergency Food Aid : It is an aid-given during emergency situations, like cases of war, natural disasters, etc., where food is distributed for free.

(iii) Project Food Aid : This is food aid delivered as part of a specific project related to promoting agricultural or economic development, nutrition and food security.

However, there are a few problems associated with the food aid :

(a) It is a system driven by the donor or giver.

(b) It might encourage donor countries to expect benefits from the recipients.

(c) It is a foreign policy tool.

International unions, NGOs, few private sectors and few government bodies are putting efforts and take initiatives to mitigate food scarcity. The food problem has been high on the international agenda for the past two years. The food crisis has become a complex problem due to the involvement of many factors and ignorance and lack of understanding, the seriousness of the situation. Many more private sectors, government bodies along with the citizens should come forward with an objective fostering of constructive and holistic development of our country as well as our planet.

SUMMARY

- Sustainable agriculture is a farming practice which incorporates sustainable practices by considering ecosystem services.
- IPM is an integral component of crop management which looks at all aspects necessary to grow a crop.
- A genetically modified organism (GMO) is any organism whose genetic material has been altered using genetic engineering techniques.
- The HYV crops respond better to fertilizers and pesticides compared to the usual crops.
- Appropriate cropping pattern and farming practice can be implemented to increase the crop yield without comprising the land quality for future agriculture.
- Agroforestry is a land use management system in which trees or shrubs are grown around or among crops or pastureland.
- Tillage or field ploughing is a very important step in agriculture.
- Irrigation is the artificial application of water to soil, in the correct amounts and frequency, for optimal soil infiltration and plant growth.
- The Integrated Nutrient Management aims at integrating the use of natural and man-made soil nutrients to increase crop productivity and preserve soil productivity for future generations.
- The world produces enough food to feed everyone, however due to inefficient economic systems, a biased food distribution is seen.

- Food aid refers to the provision of food or cash to purchase food in times of emergency or to provide longer-term solutions in areas where food shortages exist.

EXERCISE

A. Define each of these terms :

1. Genetically modified crops
2. Mixed cropping
3. Tillage farming
4. Crop rotation
5. Green manures
6. Gene banks

B. Answer in brief :

1. State the difference between the transgenic plants and Genetically modified crops.
2. Write any two ill effects of Genetic engineering on environment.
3. Write any two drawbacks of hybrid seeds.
4. What are the criteria that should be checked while selecting the crops for mixed cropping?
5. Differentiate between intercropping and mixed cropping.
6. What is bio-fertilizer?
7. Explain the types of gene banks.
8. List the types and objectives of gene banks.

C. Answer the following in detail :

1. Explain the types of food aid.
2. Explain the processing of sewage sludge to produce manure for agriculture.
3. List out any six advantages of drip irrigation.
4. Explain the types of conservation tillage
5. Write the four principles of regenerative farming.

D. Previous Year's Board Questions :

1. Define silviculture.
2. Mention any two benefits of Green Manure.
3. How does biotechnology play an important role in achieving global food security?
4. What is regenerative farming?
5. What are HYVs? State any two advantages and two disadvantages of HYVs.
6. Explain five methods of achieving sustainable agriculture.
7. What do you understand by 'Gene Banks'? Discuss the objectives of maintaining Gene Banks.
8. Discuss the advantages and disadvantages of conservation tillage farmin
9. Why is biotechnology used in agriculture?
10. How does the system of trickle drip irrigation operate?

WORKSHEET

A. Fill in the blanks :

1. The term 'sustainable agriculture' was first coined by Australian agricultural scientist __________.
2. The pests that survive the application of the chemicals and pass on their genes to their offspring further become ______.
3. A nematode ____________ infects the roots of tobacco plants and causes a great reduction in yield.
4. _________ is a precursor of vitamin A.

B. Give reasons for each of these statements :

1. Tillage is a very important step in agriculture.
2. A big majority of undernourished people are from developing and under–developed countries.
3. Food aid is an effective way to stabilize the food security.
4. Seeds and embryo are stored in liquid nitrogen in cryobanks.

C. Read the following excerpts and answer the questions that follow. (open-ended questions) :

1. Resham Pal is a farmer who owns a few acres of land dedicated for agriculture. He wants to try mixed cropping in his land. The choice of crops made by him for mixed cropping are rice and soya bean.

(a) Is the choice of crops made by Resham Pal is correct ? Justify your answer.

(b) Suggest few pest control techniques which could be incorporated by Resham Pal to maintain his field.

2. In early 2001, Philippines took the first step to grow the nutritional Golden Rice and make it available as an additional intervention for Vitamin A Deficiency without any additional cost compared to white rice.
   (a) Rice is a rich source of carbohydrates. How can rice be fortified with Vitamin A?
   (b) Give another example of food fortification.
3. Florida's climate makes it ideal for growing a wide variety of crops. Major crops include citrus, sugarcane, tomatoes, peppers, cotton, watermelons, peanuts, snap beans and potatoes. However, some species of weeds are prominent there, which competes for the sunlight and nutrients with crops. The alligator weed flea beetle was introduced by the farmers in the fields of Florida to counter the invasive weed species *Alternanthera philoxeroides*.

(a) How do you think this step would have helped the farmers?

(b) What could be the probable challenges faced by the farmers during weed control by introducing a predator?

D. Activities :

1. Interview a farmer and prepare a short report on kind of irrigation system, pest management strategies, fertilizers used and types of crops grown.
2. Write one case of sustainable agriculture in India.

6 BIODIVERSITY

1.0 INTRODUCTION

The Biodiversity generally refers to the variety and variability of life on Earth. Our planet Earth nourishes an enormous diversity of life. Such diverse forms of life boosts ecosystem productivity where each species, no matter how small or tiny, all have an important role to play. According to the IUCN (2004), the total number of plant and animal species described so far is more than 1.5 million, but many species are yet to be discovered and described. Although India has only 2.4 per cent of the world's land area, it contributes to 8.1 percent of the global species diversity; and our country is one of the 12 mega diversity countries of the world. Biodiversity denotes the variation at the genetic, species and the ecosystem level.

Genetic level : This is a measure of the diversity of genes in a population or species. India has more than 50,000 genetically different strains of rice, and 1,000 varieties of mango. Various species of tigers like Bengal tigers (*Panthera tigris tigris*), Indo-Chinese tiger (*Panthera tigris corbetti*), etc. exist in different places.

Species level : This is the diversity at the species level. For example, the Western Ghats have a greater amphibian species diversity than the Eastern Ghats.

Ecosystem level : This diversity denotes variation from one ecosystem to another. Organisms show various features which is the result of adaptation that has happened over millions of years of evolution. Organisms which are inhabitants of desert, mountains, polar regions, wetlands, rainforests, fresh-water, seawater, humid areas, all show different physiological features.

Millions of years of evolution has resulted in such a rich biodiversity. However, non-judicious exploitation will result in loss of biodiversity.

Fascinating Fact

According to the UN Convention on Biological Diversity, we share our planet with as many as 13 million living species, of which only 1.75 million have been named and recorded.

1.1 LOSS OF BIODIVERSITY

The **International Union for Conser-vation of Nature (IUCN)** is the world's main authority on the conservation status of species. The IUCN maintains a list called IUCN Red List of Threatened Species which contains the world's most comprehensive inventory of the global conservation status of biological species. Presently, 12 percent of all bird species, 23 per cent of all mammal species, 32 per cent of all amphibian species and 31 per cent of all gymnosperm species in the world face the threat of extinction. Surveys and statistics show that if the present trends continue, nearly half of all the species on earth might be wiped out within the next 100 years. Human activities like population explosion, urbanisation, industrialisation, etc. are resulting in decline in the biological wealth. For example, the inhabitation of tropical Pacific Islands by humans is said to have led to the extinction of more than 2,000 species of indigenous birds. The causes of loss of biodiversity are detailed below :

> **Fascinating Fact**
>
> More than 70,000 different plant species are used in traditional and modern medicine.

(i) Habitat loss, alteration and fragmentation

Human beings encroach and exploit natural habitat of plants and animals for various reasons like cultivation of crops having commercial value, extracting resources, etc. The transformation of the natural areas determines not only the loss of the vegetable species, but also a decrease in the animal species associated to them. Over few decades, we have witnessed deterioration of many forest areas. When large habitats are broken up into small fragments due to various human activities, mammals and birds requiring large territories and certain animals with migratory habits are badly affected, leading to population declines. For example, tropical rainforest covered more than 14 percent of Earth's land, which is now reduced to less than 6 percent of total Earth's land.

(ii) Over-exploitation

Human beings are depended on nature for their basic needs like food, clothing, shelter. But with technological advancements,–Human beings have explored many other uses of nature. Therefore, their need has turned into greed. Activities like hunting, fishing, etc. have led to extinction of various species which is a result of our over-exploitation of natural resources. In an ecosystem, each organism has an important role to play. Extinction or non-participation of one species considerably affects the ecological balance. The number of plants and animals appearing in the list of endangered species is increasing. An endangered species is a species which has been categorized as very likely to become extinct. For example : Siberian tiger. Passenger pigeon is already extinct as a result of overhunting.

(iii) Introduction of exotic species and genetically modified organisms

Species originating from a particular area are called exotic species. Genetically modified organisms (GMOs) are those organisms which are artificially created in the laboratory by forcing genes from the DNA of one species into the genes of an unrelated plant or animal. Introduction of such organisms into new natural environments can lead to different forms of imbalance in the ecological equilibrium. Some exotic species and GMOs turn invasive and predate or compete with indigenous species for resources, which can lead to extinction of indigenous species. The Nile perch was introduced into Lake Victoria in east Africa. It eventually led to the extinction of more than 200 species of cichlid fish in the lake.

(iv) Pollution and climate change

Human activity influences the ecological balance by altering the flow of energy, the chemical and physical constitution, climate, food chain, etc. For example, heating of the Earth's surface affects biodiversity because it endangers all the species that reside in the polar regions and mountain areas that are adapted to the cold temperature. Introduction of pollutants in air, water and soil causes harm to plants and animals residing in that vicinity. Many pollutants enter the food chain and cause bio-magnification.

(v) Co-extinctions

When a species becomes extinct, the plant and animal species associated with it in an obligatory way also become extinct. Extinction of one species disturbs the food chain as its predator will starve. Many organisms serve as hosts, pollinators while some organisms share symbiotic relationship with each other. Such parasites will also suffer extinction along with the main victim. For example : The female rhinoceros stomach, bot fly lays eggs behind the endangered black rhinoceros (*Diceros bicornis*) and the white rhinoceros (*Ceratotherium simum*) ears or horns or neck and then the flies' larvae enter the animal's digestive tract and digs into the stomach lining and then are excreted out and the life cycle restarts. Extinction of these endangered rhinoceros led to extinction of the parasite which was dependant on it for place to lay eggs and nutrition for larvae.

? Intext Questions

1. Define Biodiversity.
2. How does fragmentation lead to decline in population of certain species?
3. How does climate change induce loss of biodiversity?

1.2 NEED TO CONSERVE BIODIVERSITY

Our planet is not only the home of mankind, but of all life on the Earth. Every time a species goes extinct, we are affected. Such an effect could be direct or indirect but is certainly irreversible. All organisms have right to live and access to resources provided by the nature. Thus, man holds a greater responsibility towards preserving and conserving this heritage. The reasons and importance of conserving biodiversity is detailed as follows :

(i) Economic concerns

Humans reap innumerable direct economic benefits from nature. Besides Food (cereals, pulses, fruits), firewood, fibre, construction material, industrial products (tannins, lubricants, dyes, resins, perfumes) are few uses. Considerable percentile of the drugs is derived from plants. With increasing resources put into research activities like exploring molecular, genetic and species-level diversity for products of economic importance, nations can gain enormous benefits. Sustainable and judicious usage and extraction of natural resources is crucial to support future generations with resources.

(ii) Ecological concerns

Biodiversity is essential for the smooth functioning of cycles of ecosystems. A substantial risk of undesirable and unexpected changes in ecosystem services is posed when the abundance of any species in an ecosystem is changed greatly. Biodiversity loss damages essential services provided by the nature. Amazon forest is estimated to produce 20 per cent of total oxygen produced in the earth through the process of photosynthesis. We cannot bid any economic value for such ecosystem services. Pollination is another service, ecosystems provide through pollinators like insects, birds, animals, wind, etc. It is very difficult to accomplish these processes artificially or without intervention of nature.

(iii) Aesthetic concern

Apart from economic and ecological benefits, we also reap various intangible benefits from nature. Greenery, beautiful flower blooms, fresh fragrance of flowers and buds give us aesthetic pleasure. Many people develop a deep aesthetic appreciation for biodiversity and its functioning. This appreciation encourages many hobby activities like bird-watching, butterfly-watching; taming animals and pets, gardening and culturing exotic plants, nature photography, nature painting, eco-tourism, nature reading and writing and many more.

Production of at least one third of the world's food, depends on pollination carried out by insects, bats and birds. The cost of this eco-system service is approximately worth $200 billion annually.

1.3 CONSERVING BIODIVERSITY

It is important to realize the economical, ecological, aesthetical, legal and ethical reasons to conserve biodiversity. Plenty of organisations and environmentalists are coming up with various ways to conserve biodiversity. Understanding of patterns of diversity and the reasons for their decline in population is essential to formulate appropriate measures of conservation.

(i) In-situ conservation

When we conserve and protect the whole ecosystem, its biodiversity at all levels is protected. This approach is called in-situ (on-site) conservation. It is the process of protecting an endangered species in its natural habitat, either by protecting or restoring the habitat. To make the conservation program effective, environmentalists have identified biodiversity hotspots. A biodiversity hotspot is a biogeographic region that is both a significant reservoir of endemic species and is threatened with destruction. A large number of these hotspots can be saved from degradation through in-situ methods.

(a) Wildlife Sanctuaries

A wildlife sanctuary, is a geographic territory that provides protection for animals from hunting, predation, competition or poaching. They include a variety of ecosystems, out of which some are artificially created to support highly endangered species. Currently, there are 543 wildlife sanctuaries in India.

(b) National Parks

A national park is a park made to protect the animals that live inside it which is officially recognised, maintained and monitored by a nation's government. The largest national park in the world as defined by the IUCN is the Northeast Greenland National Park. Activities like cultivation, forestry, hunting, etc. are strictly prohibited in national parks.

(c) Biosphere reserves

Biosphere reserves are internationally recognised areas of the planet, selected by the scientific interest in their ecological, biological and cultural value. They serve various purpose like preserving genetic diversity of various biomes, unique biological communities, understanding traditional lifestyles of tribal people, etc. Each reserve promotes solutions merging the conservation of biodiversity with its sustainable use. The concept of biological reserves was initiated in 1971 by an intergovernmental scientific programme, called **Man and Biosphere (MAB).** The aim of this programme was to establish a scientific basis for the improvement of relationships between people and their environments. Biosphere reserves have three zones :

1. The core area which comprises of a strictly protected ecosystem that contributes to the conservation of landscapes, ecosystems, species and genetic variation.

2. The buffer zone which surrounds or adjoins the core areas and is used for activities compatible with sound ecological practices that can reinforce scientific research, monitoring, training and education.

3. The transition area which is the part of the reserve where the greatest activity is allowed, fostering economic and human development that is socio-culturally and ecologically sustainable.

Advantages of in-situ conservation

(i) Avoids storage problems associated with field gene banks and unmanageable seeds.

(ii) Allows evolution to continue through exposure to pests and diseases and other environmental factors.

(iii) Indirect benefits include ecosystem services.

(iv) Sustainable use by local people.

Disdvantages of in-situ conservation

(i) Requires vast area for effective conservation.

(ii) Exposes natural populations to a wide range of extreme events like cyclones, earthquakes, tsunamis, etc., and other threats.

(iii) Materials cannot be readily used and are very difficult to access.

(iv) Expensive to maintain.

(ii) Ex-situ conservation

In this approach, threatened animals and plants are taken out from their natural habitat and placed in special setting where they can be protected and given special care.

(a) Zoological Parks : A zoo or zoological park is a facility in which animals are housed within enclosures. These animals are displayed to the public also. Adequate care is taken in zoos to ensure quality food, environment and health of animals.

(b) Botanical Gardens : A botanical garden is a garden dedicated to the collection, cultivation and display of a wide range of plants. Botanical gardens are often run by universities or other scientific research organisations. The plants that might be lost in nature, are conserved in the gardens. It allows us to consider restoration and rehabilitation of degraded habitats. Botanical gardens, and zoos are the most conventional methods of Ex- situ conservation. These facilities provide not only housing and care for endangered species, but also have an educational value. They inform the public of the declining status of endangered species and of those factors which cause the threat. Such an awareness may create public interest in stopping and reversing those factors which risks the survival of species.

(c) Gene Banks : Gene banks are a type of biorepository which preserve genetic material. Gametes of threatened species can be preserved in viable and fertile condition for long periods using cryopreservation techniques, eggs can be fertilised in vitro, and plants can be propagated using tissue culture methods. Seeds of different genetic strains of commercially important plants can be kept for long periods in seed banks. To conserve agricultural biodiversity, gene banks are used to store and conserve the plant genetic resources of major crop plants. Various researches and experiments on germplasm are carried out in forestry institutions to upgrade the quality and quantity of plant products.

? Intext Questions

1. Name a few ecosystem services.
2. Differentiate between in-situ and ex-situ conservation
3. What is a gene bank ?
4. Why are Amazon forest called as lungs of the Earth ?

Advantages of ex-situ conservation

(i) Helps in conserving a variety of species from going into extinction, considering the habitat loss worldwide.

(ii) Helps in educating common public on the significance of wildlife that in turn change their behaviour and drive them into a responsible being.

(iii) Best way to raise money from public, which can be used for conservation programs and to develop technologies for conservation purposes.

(iv) Serves as a huge repository of resources for researchers who face difficulties and challenges in conducting experiments or field surveys at natural habitat.

(v) Infrastructure can be utilised for awareness and education programmes to further sensitise the public about the plants and animals, especially about the extinct species. It can be done through presentation of maps, photographs, charts, videos, etc.

Disadvantages of ex-situ conservation

(i) Behaviour of animals is affected by frequent unknown visitors, that too in huge numbers.

(ii) Animals housed in artificial habitats are defied by a wide range of potentially offensive environmental challenges such as artificial lighting, exposure to loud or disturbing noise, arousing odours and uncomfortable temperatures or substrates.

(iii) For naturally out-breeding species, the high levels of in–breeding in captivity often have negative effects on life history traits related to reproduction and survival.

(iv) For plants, ecological shifts, small population size, genetic drift, inbreeding, and gardener-induced selection may negatively affect population structure after several generations of ex-situ conservation.

(v) Although, captive breeding is a valuable process to conserve threatened species but it involves many constraints in terms of cost, workforce and reliable power source.

Harvesting wildlife for commercial needs

Human beings depend on wildlife for many products and materials. It is high time that we realize the significance and need for sustainable wildlife enterprise. A sustainable wildlife enterprise is a farming system that incorporates sustainable use of wildlife to promote conservation. The following measures can be taken to initiate and practice judicious wildlife harvesting :

(i) Hunting in hotspots should be banned.

(ii) Hunting should be banned in the breeding season.

(iii) We should not hunt young or pregnant animals.

(iv) Habitats of migratory animals should be protected.

(v) There should be a capping over quantity of animal products manufactured on all countries. This will prevent over exploitation.

(vi) The hunter must have a license.

(vii) People must be made aware of the current scenario of biodiversity and importance to conserve it.

Biodiversity knows no political boundaries and its conservation is therefore a collective responsibility of all nations and all citizens.

1.4 CONSERVATION STRATEGIES AT THE NATIONAL AND INTERNATIONAL LEVEL

Imposing appropriate laws and regulation is essential for conserving biodiversity at the national and international levels. Several international organisations like IUCN, UNESCO, etc. are collaboratively functioning with national governments to conserve biodiversity.

Some of them are detailed below :

1. Wildlife Protection Act (1972)

The Wildlife Protection Act, 1972 is an Act of the Parliament of India enacted for protection of plants and animal species. The Act aims to provide protection for wild animals, birds and plants; and also concerns with the matters connected with wildlife. It extends to the whole of India, except the State of Jammu and Kashmir which has its own Wildlife Act. It has six schedules which give varying degrees of protection.

2. Project Tiger, 1973

Project Tiger is a tiger conservation programme launched in 1973 by the Government of India. The project aims at ensuring a viable population of Bengal tigers in their natural habitats and also to protect them from extinction. The project also aimed at preserving areas of biological importance and natural heritages. Project tiger worked on measures to mitigate the factors that led to decline in tiger's population.

3. IUCN

It is a membership union composed of both government and civil society organisations. It provides public, private and non-governmental organisations with the knowledge and tools that enable human progress, economic development and nature conservation to take place together. It works on six major concerns dedicated to species survival, environmental law, protected areas, social and economic policy, ecosystem management, and education and communication. IUCN also maintains the red data book which consists of all information about extinct and endangered species.

4. The Ramsar Convention on Wetlands (1971)

The Ramsar Convention on Wetlands of International Importance is an international treaty for the conservation and sustainable use of wetlands. It is named after the city of Ramsar in Iran, where the Convention was signed in 1971. The mission of the Ramsar Convention is to conserve and monitor the use of all wetlands in a sustained manner through local, regional and national actions and international cooperation.

5. CITES

CITES (The Convention on International Trade in Endangered Species of Wild Fauna and Flora) is an international agreement between governments. Its aim is to ensure that international trade in specimens of wild animals and plants does not threaten their survival. It also accords varying degrees of protection to more than 35,000 species of animals and plants.

6. The Convention on Biodiversity

The Convention on Biological Diversity (CBD) is a multilateral treaty, which has three main goals: the conservation of biodiversity, sustainable use of its components and the fair and equitable sharing of benefits arising from genetic resources. Its objective is to develop national strategies for the conservation and sustainable use of biological diversity.

- The Biodiversity generally refers to the variety and variability of life on Earth.
- Biodiversity denotes the variation at the genetic, species and the ecosystem level.
- Habitat loss, fragmentation, over exploitation, pollution, climate change, introduction of alien species and co-extinctions are reasons for loss in biodiversity.
- Biodiversity provides us various economic, ecological and aesthetic benefits.
- It is important to realise the economical, ecological, aesthetical, legal and ethical reasons to conserve biodiversity.
- Biodiversity conservation can be done by in-situ and ex-situ methods.
- When we conserve and protect the whole ecosystem, then this approach is called insitu (on-site) conservation. However, when there are situations where an animal or plant is endangered or threatened and needs urgent measures to save it from extinction, ex-situ (off site) conservation is the desirable approach.
- Imposing appropriate rules and regulate to mitigate over exploitation of wildlife is essential.
- Acts and conventions like The Wildlife Protection Act, The Ramsar Convention, Project Tiger, CBD aims at conserving biodiversity.

- Organisations like UNEP, UNESCO, IUCN, etc collaborate with National governments to initiate and conduct various programs with an objective to combat various issues related to environment and nature.

A. Define each of these terms :

1. Biodiversity
2. Biosphere
3. CITES

B. Answer the following in brief :

1. Explain the aesthetic value of biodiversity.
2. Explain the functioning and goals of Project tiger.
3. How is Biodiversity important in ecosystem functioning?
4. How does GMOs and exotic species lead to loss of biodiversity?
5. What is the Red Data Book ?
6. Give the full form of IUCN and give its major objectives.

C. Answer the following in detail :

1. Explain the variation at genetic, species and ecosystem level?
2. What is co-extinction? Explain giving an example.
3. Suggest measures to combat over-exploitation of wildlife.
4. Give the importance of the following :
   (a) Zoological parks
   (b) Botanical gardens
   (c) Wildlife sanctuaries
   (d) National parks
5. Give three advantages and disadvantages of :
   (a) In-situ conservation
   (b) Ex-situ conservation

D. Previous Years Board questions :

1. Distinguish between a core zone and a buffer zone in a Biosphere reserve.
2. Expand IUCN. State any one important function of IUCN.
3. What do you understand by Gene Banks? Discuss the objectives of maintaining Gene Banks.

WORKSHEET

(A) Write the zoological names of each of these animals :

1. Bengal tiger is ______.
2. Black rhinoceros ________.
3. Indo-Chinese tiger ________.
4. White rhinoceros ________.

(B) Justify the following statements (open-ended questions) :

1. Aesthetic concern is one of the reasons for conserving biodiversity.
2. A large number of hotspots can be saved through in-situ conservation.
3. Habitats of migratory animals should be protected.
4. People's participation is crucial for conserving biodiversity.

(C) Read the following excerpts and answer the questions that follow. (open-ended questions) :

(1) In 1971, UNESCO launched MAB Programme to establish a scientific basis for the improvement of relationships between people and their environments. The biosphere reserves were categorised into three zones.

(a) Which zone involved maximum people's participation and interaction?

(b) How can we foster development that is socio-culturally and ecologically sustainable?

(2) Black buck is an endangered animal. Poaching black buck is an offense which has legal consequences of imprisonment and penalty.

(a) On what basis are animals termed as endangered species?

(b) In which ways endangered animals are protected?

(D) Activities :

(1) Research and prepare a report on any two examples of co-extinction.

(2) Research and prepare a report on any five international conventions and treaties signed by India which aim at conserving biodiversity.

7 ENERGY

1.0 INTRODUCTION

Energy is the capacity or power to do work. Energy exists in various forms and ranges like kinetic energy, potential energy, mechanical energy, thermal energy, light energy, nuclear energy and electrical energy and so on. Power is defined as a rate at which work is done or energy is converted to the usable or other form. Work is done when force is applied and the object is moved to a distance. Work is done, when an energy source provides power so that the force can be applied to move an object to certain distance. Therefore, it is understood that the terms Energy, Power and Work are interconnected. All the activities that are carried in this universe require energy. Even the life processes in the bodies of living beings need energy. Adenosine Tri-Phosphates (ATP) are the energy currencies in our body.

The generation of ATP is a consequence of series of energy transformations. The sunlight from solar energy initiates the photosynthesis of glucose and other nutrients in the plants. The glucose and other nutrients enter the food chain and it passes on to various animals. The Glucose is converted to ATP via life process. The stored ATP gives us power to perform different work. This is an example of energy transformation from solar energy to chemical energy and then to mechanical energy. Hence, the energy should be transformed into a required form before harnessing it to carry out any work. As stated by the law of conservation of energy 'Energy can neither be destroyed nor be created. It can be only transformed from one form to another'. Energy is used for five main sectors, *i.e.*, residential, commercial, industrial, transportation and defense. We have been harnessing various forms of energy for numerable activities since centuries.

The energy demand is reaped from natural resources like coal, petroleum, natural gas, sunlight, water, wind, biomass, etc. Out of these sources some are renewable sources of energy while some are non-renewable sources of energy. Renewable sources of energy will get replenished and are not exhausted by the human use, like sunlight, water, wind, geothermal energy, etc. unlike non-renewable sources of energy which get exhausted after

Fascinating Fact

According to the Food and Agriculture Organization of the United Nations, the average minimum energy requirement per person per day is about 1,800 kcal.

being extracted continuously and extensively like coal, petroleum, natural gas, etc. In fact, the coal, petroleum and natural gas are being continuously formed under the below layers of crust. But this is a very slow process. The rate at which these materials are being extracted is much higher than the rate at which these materials are formed. For that reason, the planning and execution of energy conservation and using alternative sources of energy is the need of the hour.

1.1 FOSSIL FUELS PRODUCE ELECTRICITY

Fossil fuels are formed by anaerobic decomposition of remains of dead plants and animals. This process takes millions of years. Petrol, Diesel, Compressed Natural Gas and Coal are the forms of fossil fuels. The recently conducted survey indicates that fossil fuels supplies around 80% of the energy demand. Energy produced by any substance is expressed in terms of calorific value. Caloric value is the amount of energy produced by the complete combustion of a material or fuel. The energy is measured in terms joules or kilo joules. The calorific value of fossil fuel is quite high, which is the main reason as to why fossil fuels are used to produce electricity.

(i) Production of electricity

The electricity is produced in power stations. Some primary source of energy like fossil fuel, flowing water or wind is used to rotate large machines called turbines at a high speed. The large magnets are fitted in the turbines within the copper wire coils. The moving magnets within the coil of wire cause charged particles to move within the wire. This way electricity is produced. The power plants are set up where fossil fuels are burnt to generate steam. The steam thus generated rotates large turbines to produce electricity. A series of change in forms of energy can be observed here *i.e.*, Chemical energy → Heat/ Thermal energy → Mechanical energy → Electrical energy. An immense amount of steam is required to rotate huge turbines. Combustion of fossil fuels gives that energy.

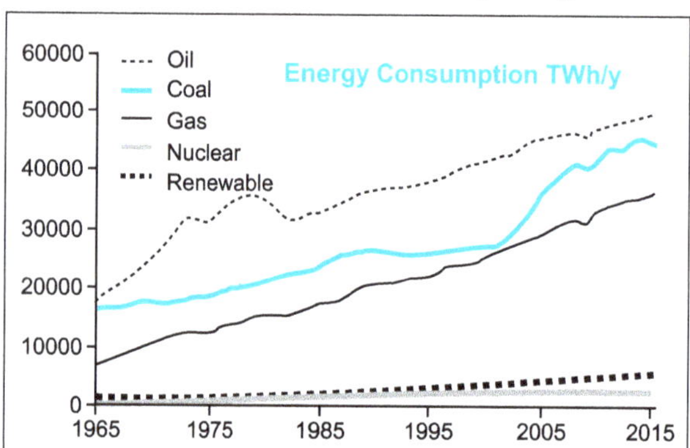

(ii) Energy Demand

World energy consumption is the total energy used by the entire human civilization. It involves all energy harnessed from every energy source applied towards human activities across every single industrial and technological sector, across every country. The graph shows the world energy consumption until the year 2015. The survey and research statistics shows that the industrial sector currently consumes around half of all global energy and feedstock fuels, with residential and commercial buildings (29%) and transport (20%) accounting for the remainder. According to the data given by the International Energy Agency (IEA) the world's demand for energy grew by 2.1 percent in 2017, more than twice the previous year's rate.

(iii) Need for renewable sources of energy

As we know, the energy demand for the over growing population is increasing exponentially. The fossil fuel reserves are being continuously exploited and evacuated. The consequences of burning fossil fuels like environmental pollution, resource depletion and disturbed ecosystem functioning cannot be ignored. Therefore, it is essential to discover and use alternative sources of energy. Fossil fuel is one of the non-renewable energy. Renewable sources of energy are those which do not deplete or get exhausted even after continuous usage. On the contrary, renewable sources of energy get exhausted or require a long time to replenish. For the production of electricity, energy is required to rotate the turbines at high speed. This energy can be routed through many renewable sources of energy like hydropower, wind, geothermal, nuclear energy, etc.

(iv) Dwindling supplies of fossil fuels

The coal and oil deposits are 150 to 300 million year old. But we have consumed a substantial amount of these deposits in the period of 200 years. There are three types of fossil fuels–oil, gas and coal. In 1880, coal was first used to produce electricity. By 1960s fossils fuels had become a major fuel to generate electricity for domestic and commercial or industrial purposes. The graph shows future energy reserves for coal, gas and oil. Between 2013 and 2040, natural gas consumption is expected to increase by 13.4 percent and coal consumption by 5.6 percent.In a recent research it was said that, in the year 2008, the world pumped out 31 billion barrels of oil. World reserves of conventional oil are in a free fall, decreasing every year.

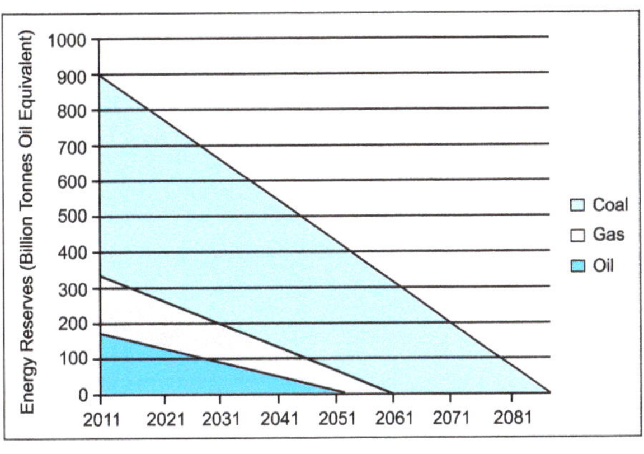

Intext Questions

1. How are the terms work, power and energy related?
2. Write the series of energy transformations occurring during the combustion of fuel to produce electricity.
3. List out some environmental problems of combustion of fossil fuels.

1.2 NUCLEAR ENERGY

When a nuclear reaction occurs, it releases nuclear energy. This energy can be harnessed to produce heat to operate steam turbines and generate electricity. Nuclear energy is produced in a nuclear reactor or a power plant. Nuclear reactions are of two types *i.e.* nuclear fission and nuclear fusion. Nuclear fusion is the process of making a single heavy nucleus from two lighter nuclei. It releases a large amount of energy. Fusion happens in the Sun. Hydrogen atoms are fused together to make Helium. This releases lots of energy in the form of light and heat. Nuclear fusion is the source of energy for the sun and stars. A power plant is a series of machines that controls nuclear reactions under controlled conditions to produce electricity. It is estimated that in the core of the sun, approximately 620 million metric tons of hydrogen atoms are fused every second. However, nuclear fission is the opposite phenomenon to the nuclear fusion. The pellets of uranium are used as nuclear fuels to run the power plants. Nuclear energy originates from the splitting of uranium atoms through a process called fission. Nuclear fission is nuclear reaction which proceeds through the radioactive decay process in which the nucleus of an atom splits into lighter nuclei.Uranium atoms splits releasing energy and the fuel becomes hot. This temperature heats the water turning it into steam. The steam turns the turbine. The turbine further turns a generator and electricity is produced. The electricity is directed to the transformers to get the appropriate voltage. The uranium left behind in the reactor after energy is harnessed and it is called as solid nuclear waste.

> **Fascinating Fact**
>
> On **June 27, 1954**, the USSR's Obninsk Nuclear Power Plant became the world's first nuclear power plant to generate electricity for a power grid and produced around 5 megawatts of electric power.

The advantages and disadvantages of harnessing nuclear energy is tabulated below :

Advantages	Disadvantages
The generation of electricity through nuclear energy reduces the amount of fossil fuel extraction and exploitation.	Management of nuclear waste is difficult. The radiations from radioactive materials are ionizing radiations which can damage living cells.
Nuclear energy does not emit greenhouse gases and other pollutants. Thus, it is a cleaner source of energy.	The nuclear power plants have a limited life. So, after a certain they have to dismantled and re-built. Therefore, the maintenance cost becomes more.
A small quantity of nuclear fuel can produce more energy. Therefore, the	Not all countries have Uranium deposits. Therefore, the countries

energy yield is more in case of nuclear energy than the fossil fuels.	which do not have uranium deposits will have to import the Uranium pellets. Importing a radioactive metal needs a robust safety management, which could be complicated and expensive.
Production of energy is continuous. A nuclear power plant generates electricity for atleast 90% of the annual time.	A chain of nuclear fission occurs in the nuclear reactor. In case the machinery breaks down or any other kind of defect is encountered, it may lead to uncontrolled chain reaction causing a huge explosion.

The functioning and management of nuclear power plant is a very complex task. It has various safety concerns which needs to be taken care of. The safety concerns for the nuclear power plants are as follows :

(i) Accidents caused due to human error : Human error can occur at every stage of the functioning of the nuclear power plant which includes process planning, execution, deployment of responsibilities, appointing efficient workforce, maintenance, checking, monitoring and data interpretation. Extreme diligence has to be done in each and every process listed here. It should be taken care the efficient and qualified people are hired for doing this job. The employees and workers should be regularly given trainings to improve their skills.

Fascinating Fact

In August 1945, the United States dropped two atomic bombs on the Japanese cities Hiroshima and Nagasaki, marking the first disastrous impact from nuclear energy. Tsar Bomba, the most powerful nuclear weapon ever detonated, was so powerful that it created seismic shocks that were measurable even on their third passage around the Earth.

(ii) Disposal of nuclear waste : Storage and disposal of nuclear waste is a big challenge for the industry. If the nuclear waste is not handled properly, Then there is always a risk of soil and water pollution and contamination. Nuclear waste also has devastating effects on the lives of plants and animals. These radiations can alter the genetic makeup of the living beings. Some of the common ways of nuclear waste disposal are as follows :

(a) Incineration : This method involves burning radioactive waste through incinerators developed for this purpose. Incineration is commonly done for the low-level waste, as this material usually consists of clothing, tubes, rags and such materials.

(b) Storage : The nuclear material decays with time. Therefore, the nuclear waste is stored in safe containers and allowed to decay until it is no longer radioactive. This process is called radioactive decay. The amount of time the material takes should be considered before executing this option.

(c) Shallow Burial : Some highly radio-active material is buried in a specially-crafted spot nearby the power plant itself. The waste is piled in the pit and covered with a non-permeable material like clay. The pile is supported by a mix of rocks and soil so that it does not erode.

(d) Deep Burial : High-level waste is buried in deep pits. Underground laboratories are built to monitor usage and storage of the materials.

(e) In Water : Special pond or special pools are constructed near the power plants, which can store fuel that has already been used for the process of generating power.

(f) Recycling : For some radioactive material, such as uranium and plutonium elements have long lives that can be processed or extracted for reuse.

(iii) Natural disasters : Nuclear power plant has to be safeguarded in case of any natural disasters. Calamities like earthquake, tsunami, storm, hurricanes or even bad weather conditions like heavy rains may affect the power plant. Such calamities may cause the breakdown of the power plant. Breakdown of power plant may have disastrous effects like short circuit, leakage of fuel, explosion, collapse, etc. Therefore, emergency management plan should be designed in advance for the power plants.

(iv) Security issues : Nuclear power plants are a potential target for terrorist operations. An attack on the power plant could cause major explosions, risking the lives on the entire locality, and expelling hazardous radioactive material into the atmosphere, soil and water.

The Chernobyl Disaster : A Catastrophic nuclear accident Chernobyl is the city situated in northern Ukraine. A nuclear power plant was set-up here, to cater the energy needs of the nearby places. The explosion happened in the early hours of Saturday 26 April 1986 within the Nuclear Power Plant. It released large quantities of radioactive contamination into the atmosphere, which spread over much of Western USSR and Europe. The explosion happened during a routine system check which was being conducted by the engineers. The safety systems of the plant were ignored during the systems check, which was one of the prime reasons for the explosion. There was a sudden flow of power output. When an emergency shutdown was attempted a more extreme spike in power output occurred, which led a reactor vessel to rupture and a series of explosions took place. The resulting fire sent a cloud of highly radioactive smoke into the atmosphere over an extensive geographical area. The cloud went on to drift over large parts of the western Soviet Union and Europe. From 1986 to 2000, over

350,000 people were evacuated and resettled from the most severely contaminated areas of Belarus, Russia, and Ukraine. 31 deaths are directly attributed to the accident, all among the reactor staff and emergency workers. The Russian publication, estimated that 985,000 premature cancer deaths occurred worldwide between 1986 and 2004 as a result of radioactive contamination from Chernobyl. The harmful effects caused by the disastrous nuclear explosion are :

(i) High thyroid doses were estimated in infants and adults.

(ii) A sevenfold increase in DNA mutations has been identified in children of liquidators conceived after the accident.

(iii) Some long-term effects like Downs syndrome and other genetic mutations.

(iv) Twenty-five years after the incident, restriction orders had remained in place in the production, transportation and consumption of food contaminated by Chernobyl fallout.

(v) It is unknown whether fallout contamination will have any long-term adverse effect on the flora and fauna of the region, as plants and animals have significantly different and varying radiologic tolerance compared with humans.

? Intext Questions

1. What is a power plant?
2. Differentiate between nuclear fission and nuclear fusion.
3. What are the security issues of the nuclear power plant?

1.3 A SUSTAINABLE ENERGY FUTURE

The main reason for the energy crisis is over consumption of energy resources. If this problem is ignored now then our future generations will be deprived of the basic amenity like electricity, fuel, etc. Energy conservation is what will save our planet and give our future generation a better place to live in. Using alternative sources of energy can contribute a lot in energy conservation and population control. Alternative sources of energy are the ones which do not cause any undesirable consequences to the environment and are renewable. Scientists around the world are researching on developing and discovering new alternative energy sources so that the growing energy needs of human population can be met more easily, safely and efficiently. Below given are some alternative sources of energy :

(i) Solar energy : Solar energy is the energy that is produced by the sun in the form of heat and light. Solar panels absorb the sunlight through the photovoltaic cells, generating Direct Current (DC) energy and then converting it to usable Alternating Current (AC) energy with the help of inverter technology. The AC is then carried to the electrical panel and distributed accordingly. The advantages and disadvantages of solar energy are as follows :

Advantages	Disadvantages
Renewable and inexhaustible source of energy.	Solar panels occupy a lot of space.
It is a clean source of energy and does not emit any pollutant into the atmosphere, soil or water.	Efficiency and yield of electricity produced is less than that of fossil fuels.
It reduces the dependence on the fossil fuels.	Solar panels cannot work efficiently during the rainy or cloudy days.
Once solar panels are fitted, the energy harnessed is absolutely free.	The initial cost of setting up a solar power plant or panel is high.
Once solar panels or lights are installed, it does not cost much to maintain them.	The efficiency of solar appliance is less in the night time.

(ii) Wind energy : Wind energy refers to the energy extracted from the blowing wind which is used to generate electricity. Wind is caused by the uneven heating of the atmosphere by the sun, variations in the earth's surface and rotation of the earth.

When the blowing wind hits the blades of the wind mill, the blades rotate. The rotating blades have kinetic energy. Wind turbines convert the kinetic energy of the wind into mechanical power. A generator can convert mechanical power into electricity. Wind farms are installed in the windy areas to harness electricity. A wind farm is a group of wind turbines in the same location used to produce electricity. A large wind farm may consist of several hundred individual wind turbines. The advantages and disadvantages of wind energy are as follows :

Fascinating Fact

India ranks fourth amongst the wind-energy-producing countries of the world after Germany, Spain and USA.

Advantages	Disadvantages
Wind energy is renewable source of energy.	For a wind turbine to be efficient, the location where it is built needs to have an adequate supply of wind energy. Therefore, the yield of electricity produced keeps fluctuating depending on the wind speed.

It is a clean source of energy and does not emit any pollutant into the atmosphere, soil or water.	Initial installation of wind farms is expensive and requires a lot of pre-planning and landscape study to be done.
It reduces the dependence on the fossil fuels.	Wind mills generate a lot of noise. Single wind turbine can be heard from hundreds of meters away.
Once the wind mills are installed, the energy harnessed is absolutely free.	The average efficiency of wind turbine is very less as compared to fossil fuel power plants.
The maintenance cost of wind mills is low.	Birds get killed or injured when they fly into turbines.
Wind turbines can be built on existing farms or ranches. Farmers and ranchers can continue to work on the land.	Wind mills have to be installed only in windy and hilly area. The wind speed has to be 10-15 m/s for proper functioning of the wind mill. Therefore, wind energy cannot be harnessed in all places.

(iii) Hydroelectricity : Hydropower is the power derived from the energy of falling water or fast running water, which may be harnessed for useful purposes. Hydroelectricity is the electricity produced from the hydropower. The dams are built to block a river. At this point, the stored water will have potential energy. When the water is released, the pressure behind the dam forces the water down pipes that lead to a turbine. The flowing water has kinetic energy. This causes the turbine to turn and rotate. This turns the generator which makes electricity.

The electricity thus harnessed can be supplied to the nearby homes. The advantages and disadvantages of hydroelectricity are as follows :

Advantages	Disadvantages
Once a dam is constructed, electricity can be produced at a constant rate. If electricity is not needed, the channel gates can be shut and the water can be saved for using another time when electricity demand is high.	Dams are extremely expensive to build and must be built to a very high standard.

It is a renewable source of energy.	The river ecosystem might get disturbed.
It is the clean source of energy which does not produce any pollutants.	People living in villages and towns that are in the valley to be flooded, must move out. This means that they lose their farms and businesses.
Once the dam is constructed, the energy harnessed is absolutely free.	Building a large dam alters the natural water table level.
The lake that forms behind the dam can be used for water sports and leisure activities or alternatively the water can be used for irrigation or supplied to nearby villages.	The hydroelectric power is dependent on the availability of water. However, when drought comes, the amount of water supply will be limited. Thus, the yield of electricity will be less.

(iv) Geothermal energy : Geothermal energy is the heat energy generated and stored inside the earth. The central layer of the earth *i.e.,* magma and core are extremely hot which consists of the molten rocks. Due to the heat of the magma ground water becomes very hot and emerges as hot springs or geysers at some places on the surface of the earth. Sometimes the hot water becomes trapped below the surface as a geothermal reservoir. Wells can be drilled into the geothermal reservoirs to generate electricity from geothermal energy. The hot water that rises emerges at the surface as steam.

Fascinating Fact

Geothermal power plants in the Philippines and Iceland contribute around 30% of their electricity production. In some parts of Iceland, hot water runs from geothermal power plants under pavements and roads to help melt ice.

The steam is used to drive turbines roducing electricity. The advantages and is advantages of geothermal energy are as follows :

Advantages	Disadvantages
Geothermal energy is extracted from the earth without burning fossil fuels and geothermal fields does not emit pollutants.	The cost of drilling wells to the geothermal reservoir is very expensive. The return on investment might not happen soon.

It is a constant source of energy compared to wind or solar energy.	The geothermal energy plants can setup only in few places which have hot springs.
Due to the fact that geothermal systems only have few movable parts which are sheltered inside a building, the life span of geothermal heat pump systems is relatively high.	Geothermal heat coming from the reservoir below may die down or run out of steam even after years of activity.

(v) Biomass : Biomass is fuel that is developed from organic materials which are obtained from plant-based substances. Biomass contains stored energy from the sun. Plants absorb the sun's energy in a process called photosynthesis. When biomass is burned, the chemical energy in biomass is released as heat. Biomass can be burned directly or converted to liquid biofuels or biogas that can be burned as fuels. Many of the biomass fuels used today come in the form of wood products, dried vegetation, crop residues, and aquatic plants. It is such a widely utilised source of energy, probably due to its low cost and indigenous nature, that it accounts for almost 15% of the world's total energy supply and as much as 35% in developing countries, mostly for cooking and heating. Certain crops called energy plantations are grown which gives high calorific value when burnt. Energy plantation is the practice of growing of selected species of trees and shrubs which are harvestable in a comparably shorter time and are specifically meant for fuel. These plantations help to provide wood either for cooking in homes or for industrial use, so as to satisfy local energy needs in a decentralized manner. The advantages and disadvantages of biomass are as follows :

Advantages	Disadvantages
Biomass used as a fuel reduces need for fossil fuels for the production of heat, steam and electricity for residential, industrial and agricultural use.	The biomass material needs to be burnt in order to harness energy, this leads to air pollution and adds up greenhouse gases to the atmosphere.
Biomass is a renewable resource of energy.	Over exploitation of biomass may lead to deforestation.
It is relatively cheaper and easily available. Biomass fuel is easily available in rural areas during agricultural practices like weeding, threshing, etc.	Cultivation of biomass fuels requires a lot of water. This could be difficult in the areas that have water scarcity.

(vi) Liquid fuels from Biomass : Liquid Biomass also known as "biofuel" is any kind of fluid or liquid produced from solid matter that is still growing or has been alive at some point which can be processed to produce a type of fuel. Some common biofuels are methanol, ethanol, gasohol, CNG and hydrogen.

S. No.	Fuel	Source/extracted from	Uses
1.	Methanol and Ethanol	Fermented from corn, grain and other plant matter.	Used in combustion engines.
2.	Gasohol	Petrol and ethanol.	Fuel for vehicles.
3.	CNG	Extracted from gas deposits in the deep layer of the crust.	Fuel for vehicles, industries, power plants, etc.
4.	Hydrogen	Cracking of natural gas like methane.	Fuel for industries.

Energy needs to be conserved not only to cut costs but also to preserve the resources for longer use. Energy conservation plays a significant role of lessening climate change. It helps in the replacement of non-renewable resources with renewable energy. Energy conservation is often the most inexpensive solution to energy shortages, and it is more environmentally kind alternative to increased energy production. Energy conservation ensures that future generations have access to enough resources to live comfortably and continue progressing. Saving energy should be an indispensable habit.

SUMMARY

- The law of conservation of energy states that 'Energy can neither be destroyed nor be created. It can be only transformed from one form to another'.
- Fossil fuels are formed by anaerobic decomposition of remains of dead plants and animals. This process takes millions of years. Petrol, Diesel, Compressed Natural Gas (CNG) and Coal are the forms of fossil fuels.
- Nuclear fusion is the process of making a single heavy nucleus from two lighter nuclei.
- Nuclear fission is the process in which the nucleus of an atom splits into lighter nuclei.
- Nuclear waste has devastating effects on the lives of plants and animals. Therefore, it should be properly handled and disposed.
- Alternative sources of energy are the ones which do not cause any undesirable consequences to the environment and are renewable.
- Solar energy, hydropower, wind energy, geothermal energy and biomass energy are some of the alternative sources of energy.

EXERCISE

A. Define the following :

1. Nuclear fission
2. Nuclear fusion
3. Fossil fuels
4. Nuclear energy
5. Biomass

B. Answer these questions in brief :

1. Which are the three types of fossil fuels?
2. How does nuclear reaction in the sun and stars occurs?
3. How is energy harnessed from the wind?
4. How can solar energy used to produce electricity?
5. What is geothermal energy?

C. Answer these questions in detail :

1. Explain the working of nuclear power plant.
2. List out the safety concerns of the nuclear power plant.
3. Which are the various ways of disposing nuclear waste?
4. Write down the advantages and disadvantages of wind energy.
5. Write down the advantages and disadvantages of solar energy.
6. Tabulate the sources and uses of any four liquid fuels.

D. Previous years board questions :

1. State two limitations of biomass as an energy resource.
2. Name alternate fuel in liquid form. Give one advantage of using it.
3. When did Chernobyl disaster occur? State the harmful effects caused by the radioactive pollution in Chernobyl disaster.
4. What are energy plantations?
5. Explain three advantages and two disadvantages of using alternative fuels.
6. What is energy conservation? Explain any four reasons for conserving energy.
7. What is hydropower? State any two advantages and any two disadvantages of hydropower.

WORKSHEET

(A) Fill in the blanks :

1. The amount of energy produced by the complete combustion of a material or fuel is called as __________.
2. In the nuclear fusion, hydrogen nuclei fuse to form ________.
3. The nuclear fuel used in the power plants is __________.
4. The liquid fuel which is a blend of ethanol and petrol is ________.

(B) Give reasons for each of these statements :

1. Solar heaters do not work well in the monsoon season.
2. It is difficult to grow energy plantation in the desert area.
3. Dams should be built in order to generate electricity from hydropower.
4. Wind farms are usually set-up on a hilly area.

(C) Read the following excerpts and answer the questions that follow. (open-ended questions) :

1. Sardar Sarovar dam is built on the Narmada River. Initially when this was being planned, local communities opposed this project.
   (a) List out the probable reasons as to why the local communities opposed Sardar Sarovar Dam project.
   (b) Write any two benefits that the local communities could have reaped if the Sardar Sarovar dam was built.
2. In Kaiga power plant, the nuclear waste is first stored for a few months and then buried in the shallow pits. Nuclear power plant in Kaiga dispose their nuclear waste in shallow pits covered with clay.
   (a) Why is clay used to dispose nuclear waste?
   (b) Why is the nuclear waste stored prior to the burial?
3. Ram is a farmer from a village in Punjab. He grows maize on a large scale in his fields. However, this year the quality of maize was not up to the mark. The taste of the maize also varied. His friend advised him to use this harvest for making a biofuel instead of disposing the crops.
   (a) Which type of fuels can be made from maize?
   (b) How are these fuels different from gasohol?

(D) Activities :

1. Prepare a short report on any two nuclear power plant accidents.
2. Research about the energy plantation in India and write the five names (along with the botanical names) of energy yielding crops.
3. Make a working model wind farm to depict how wind energy can be harnessed to produce electricity.

8 WASTE

1.0. INTRODUCTION

The progress in technology has made our lives and day to day chores much easier compared to the olden days. We are surrounded with plenty of products to enable smooth functioning of our tasks. However, invention and usage of these products are generating a lot of waste. Waste is any substance which is discarded after its use. It is disposed due to various reasons. Being worthless, defective, outdated are some of reasons for disposal of substances. However, waste can also become a valuable resource, if it is treated and amended properly. It can be classified under two broad areas–Biodegradable and Non-biodegradable waste. Further, waste can be of many types depending on the source or process where from it is generated. Some examples are household waste, industrial waste, medical waste, electronic waste, sanitary waste, hazardous waste, radioactive waste, etc. Waste can be also categorised based on their state *i.e.,* solid waste (garbage, electronic waste, etc.), liquid waste (sanitary waste, effluents, etc.) and gas waste (hazardous gases like NO_x, SO_x, CFC, etc released from industries, vehicles, etc.). Developed countries produce more waste as their population and rate of consumption is high. The presence of waste in our environment not only disturbs the ambience of the place, but also leads to pollution, unhygienic conditions, health effects and environmental impact. Therefore, we need effective measures to minimise waste generation and appropriately handle the waste generated from various sources.

1.1. SOLID WASTE

Solid waste includes all the wastes in solid state which may be biodegradable or non-degradable in nature.Biodegradable waste includes any organic matter in waste which can be broken down into simple organic molecules by micro-organisms and other living things during composting, aerobic digestion, anaerobic digestion or similar processes. While, non-biodegradable cannot be changed to a harmless natural state by the natural means, and may therefore damage the environment.

Fascinating Fact

Over 7 million tons of food and drink are thrown away each year.

Biodegradable solid waste includes following substances :

(i) Municipal solid waste : This includes waste from the sewerage sources.

(ii) Food and kitchen waste : The substances like left over food, vegetable and fruits peels, meat bones and skin, etc. are included in this category.

(iii) Green waste or Agricultural waste : Mulch, fodder, dry plants, twigs, removed weeds, etc. are green or agricultural waste.

(iv) Miscellaneous : Materials that are biodegradable like paper, bioplastics, etc. are one of components of biodegradable waste.

(v) Bio-medical waste : Certain waste products of hospitals like blood, tumours, organs or body parts that are removed during surgery, etc. are bio-degradable in nature. However, such wastes should be appropriately handled as it can spread diseases and infections in surrounding areas.

Fascinating Fact

India generates about 484 tonnes of biomedical waste per day.

Non-biodegradable solid waste includes following substances :

(i) Household waste : Waste materials like plastic, glass, metals are included in this category.

(ii) Electronic waste : All electronic appliances or gadgets, wires, battery cells, etc. which are disposed due to various reasons, constitute the electronic waste.

(iii) Industrial waste : An immense amount of waste generated during building and/or functioning of an industry or factory. Materials like metals, rubber, chemicals, wood, plastic, glass, parts of electronic machineries, cement, asbestos, etc. are the examples of industrial waste.

(iv) Bio-medical waste : Materials like injection syringe, plastic, cotton, bandage, Plaster of Paris, rubber, metals, faulty instruments, etc. are listed under non-degradable biomedical waste.

Intext Questions

1. List out the major types of solid waste.
2. Differentiate between biodegradable and non-biodegradable waste.
3. Why do developed countries produce more amount of waste?

1.2 WASTE DISPOSAL

Waste can be in various forms which come from various sources. Each type of waste should be handled and disposed in an appropriate manner. Waste management practices also differs from one region to another. Waste management or waste disposal includes the activities and actions required to manage waste from its inception to its final disposal. The activities include collection of waste, transport, treatment and disposal. There are various rules, regulations and constraints set for all steps of waste disposal. The legal framework has also laid down the guidelines for waste disposal and recycling. The main purpose of waste management is reducing ill effects of waste of health, environment and aesthetics.

Fascinating Fact

In the Pacific Ocean, there is a "Plastic Island" twice the size of Texas that was created by dumping waste into the ocean.

(i) Landfills

Disposing waste in landfills are one of the conventional and oldest method of waste disposal. Landfill sites are waste disposal sites where the waste materials are disposed burying. A landfill is a designed structure built into or on top of the ground, in which trash is separated from the area around it. Landfills are different from the dump. In a dump, the garbage is just buried and left unmonitored. While, in a landfill the waste material is safely separated from the environment.

Landfills are classified into three types :

(a) Municipal solid waste landfill : It is a disposal site where municipal solid, non-hazardous waste are disposed. Such landfills are accurately designed and built to ensure environmentally safe and secure disposal facilities.

(b) Sanitary landfill : Sanitary landfills are sites which collect sanitary waste and are isolated from the environment. This waste is degraded biologically, chemically and physically in the pit. They can be further made secure with the following treatments :

(i) Waste-to-energy Treatment : It is a process of generating energy in the form of electricity or heat from primary treatment of waste.

(ii) Anaerobic Digestion : It is a process by which microorganisms break down as biodegradable material in the absence of oxygen. The process is used for industrial or domestic purpose to manage and to produce fuels.

(iii) Compost : It is an organic matter that has been decomposed and recycled as a fertilizer and soil amendment. Compost is a key ingredient in organic farming.

(c) Construction and Demolition Land-fill : A huge amount of waste is produced in the process of construction like concrete, asphalt, wood, asbestos, gypsum, paper, glass and roofing materials. Such wastes go into the construction and demolition landfill.

(d) Inert landfill : Inert waste is a waste which is neither chemically nor biologically reactive and will not decompose.The examples of inert waste are products like concrete, sand, rock, bricks, etc.

Advantages of landfills are :

(i) Landfills, being a specific area of waste disposal, it is easy to monitor and maintain.

(ii) The biodegradable wastes are decomposed in the landfill. The decomposed matter can be further recycled to make manure and can be used to generate energy.

(iii) The landfill sites can be further developed into botanical gardens, parks or small plantations.

However, there are a few environmental problems associated with landfill system if they are not managed properly.

Some hazards of landfills are :

(i) Air pollution : Landfills create a threat to our environment by forming hazardous gases like methane from the landfill biodegradation. Methane is a potent greenhouse gas. There are over ten toxic gases released from landfills. Methane gas is naturally produced during the process of decay of organic matter. As methane gas is formed, it builds up pressure and then begins to move through the soil.

(ii) Groundwater pollution : The landfills pollute groundwater by leaching the waste into the underground water. The major issue caused with landfill leachates is the leakage of a large number of toxins into fresh waterways, which ultimately reaches our homes as drinking water or water for everyday use.

(iii) Incinerator : A waste treatment process which includes the combustion of waste for recovering the energy is called as incineration. When the process of incineration is coupled with high temperatures, it is termed as thermal treatment. Incinerators convert waste materials into heat, gas, steam and ash. These products are further used to produce energy. Incineration is carried out both on a small scale by individuals and on a large scale by industry. It is used to dispose of solid, liquid and gaseous waste. In earlier days, incineration was carried out without segregation of materials, thus, causing harm to environment. This resulted in risk for plant workers health and environment. Incineration is a controversial method of waste disposal, as it has some advantages as well as disadvantages.

Benefits of incinerators are :

(i) Incinerators occupy less space compared to landfills. In densely populated areas or small towns, where there is insufficiency of land space, identification and selection of site for landfills could be difficult task. In such conditions, mounting an incinerator is a better option.

(ii) The mass of solid wastes can be reduced by 80% to 90% by employing incinera-tion.

(iii) Incineration plants are capable for producing energy and can substitute other power generation plants.

(iv) It is a feasible method of disposing of certain hazardous waste materials like biological medical waste.

Drawbacks of incinerators are :

(i) Incineration facilities are expensive to build, operate and maintain. These facilities also require skilled staff to run and maintain them.

(ii) Incinerators are not feasible for places which, majorly generate organic or biodegradable wastes. Citizens and municipality authorities should be encouraged to make compost from biodegradable wastes, rather than burning it.

(iii) The emissions from incinerators include toxic materials like nitrogen oxide, heavy metals, particulates, furan, dioxin, etc. Out of these some materials are potent carcinogens. These emissions also have adverse effects on environment, like pollution and global warming.

? Intext Questions

1. Explain the term sanitary landfill.
2. How do landfills lead to groundwater pollution ?
3. List out the toxic materials emitted by the incinerators.

1.3 SOLID WASTE : OPTIONS FOR FUTURE

The waste management has substantial impact on our environment, health and the well-being. For decades, waste management was perceived at a very superficial level. Waste management was the simple disposal of waste materials to landfills or other designated sites. But now, much change is seen in how waste disposal is viewed has been impacted by a growing consciousness of a healthy environment. With immense progress in technology, there are radical changes in methods of waste management.

(i) The 3R principle (Reduce, Re-use and Recycle)

The 3R method is one of the most efficient methods to prevent waste generation.

(a) Reduce : Generation of the waste should be reduced at the source. Waste is often created due to inefficient use of resource or bad planning of procuring new materials.If we do not plan our purchases properly, we will end up in overconsumption of goods, which further keeps generating more and more waste. Therefore, monitoring and reducing our purchases and consumption appropriately is the first and significant step towards waste management.

(b) Reuse : Instead of throwing away articles after its use, we can try to find various other efficient ways to reuse it. For example, donating old clothes, toys and furniture to the needy and poor, using both sides of writing paper, etc. The waste articles can be also put to other uses after some modifications. For instances, plastic bottle can be made into a pen stand, home décor articles can be made from used cardboards or plastic containers, some plastic or glass containers like jam bottles can be used for storage purpose. However, this requires some creativity.

(c) Recycle : It is the key component of the 3R principle of waste management. Recycling is the process of changing the waste and non-useable materials into potentially useful materials. Recycling reduces the consumption of raw materials and energy usage. Paper, plastic, glass, magazines, electronics, and more can be processed into new products while using fewer natural resources and less energy.

(ii) Below listed are few ways that can be followed in day to day to Reduce, Reuse and Recycle :

(i) Reduce :

(a) Avoid buying over-packaged goods, which contains packing of foil, paper, and plastic.

(b) Avoid buying disposable or throwaway goods like paper plates, cups, razors, pens, etc.

(c) Prefer durable items over short term use articles. Such items will last longer and do not add up to the quantity of waste material.

(d) Use electronic mail or communication rather than written messages.

(e) Digital media like e-books, e-newspapers, e-magazines, etc. contribute in reduction of paper waste.

(ii) Reuse :

(a) We should try to save paper and plastic bags and carry them when we go for shopping. Thus we can avoid asking or buying new plastic or paper bags.

(b) Plastic containers can be reused to store items.

(c) Old clothes, appliances, toys, and furniture can be donated to charities instead of disposing.

(iii) Recycle :

(a) Give preference for purchasing recycled items like storage containers, home decors, papers, books, etc.

(b) Collect information about the scrap dealers or recycling unit located in the vicinity of your home or workplace. Give away the waste materials like metal cans, newspapers, paper products, glass, plastics to those units for recycling.

(c) Composting : Composting is a way of harnessing the natural process of decomposition to speed up the decay of waste. Composting is one very old methods of getting rid of organic waste, which was commonly followed by the farmers. Kitchen waste, animal excreta and other decaying waste were buried in small pits in the backyards. However, nowadays, composting is done on commercial basis. Composting method has shown positive as well as negative effects. These are detailed below :

Benefits of composting are :

(i) Through composting the amount of garbage sent to the landfill is reduced.

(ii) The organic matter is reused rather than dumped.

(iii) It is a low cost and simple method of waste management.

(iv) During composting, the waste matter is decomposed and broken down into nutrients by various decomposers. These nutrients replenish the fertility of the soil.

(v) Composting also improves soil profile by increasing aeration, water infiltration, retention of sandy soil and re-establishing the proper functioning of the soil ecosystem.

Drawbacks of composting are :

(i) It can be inconvenient to gather the biodegradable waste. As the waste start rotting, it starts smelling.

(ii) Rotting matter can attract many insects and vectors of various infectious diseases. Thus, making the surrounding unhygienic and unsafe.

(iii) Composting is the time-consuming process. Approximately a time of one to three months is required to form a compost. Climatic conditions may alter this period.

(iii) Vermiculture : Vermiculture means artificial rearing or cultivation of worms especially Earthworms for decomposing biodegradable substances. The compost made by worms is called as vermicompost. Vermicompost involves composting a mixture of decomposing food waste, bedding materials and vermicast. Along with earthworms, white worms and red wiglers are also used for vermicomposting. Vermicomposting can be also applied for sewage treatment. Vermicompost is an excellent organic fertilizer and improves the soil texture. It does not involvese laborated procedures and high cost. However, there are few challenges involved in vermicomposting during its operation and maintenance, like :

(a) Moisture level of 70-85% must be maintained. If the moisture level falls, the respiration of the worms will be difficult leading to worm mortality.

(b) Protection of worms from pests and predators like rodents and ants is difficult. The smell of rotting matter attracts many insects too. It is difficult to maintain hygiene of these place.

(c) Many a times worms escape out of the compost container.

(iv) Biotechnology : Biotechnology finds its significant application in many sectors. Biotechnology is used to solve various environmental problems, out of which one is the waste management. Bioremediation is a process used to treat contaminated media, including water, soil and subsurface material, by altering environmental conditions to stimulate the growth of microorganisms and degrade the target pollutants. Process like fermentation, redox reaction and denitrification are used to convert waste material into less harmful and less contaminating substances. Anaerobic and Aerobic bioremediation is used to get rid of hydrocarbons, oils, etc. By using certain pathways of some microbes, even the heavy metals like cadmium can be removed from the environment.

Limitations of bioremediation are :

(a) These reactions are highly specific. It is difficult to understand the complexities of pathways of microbes, which makes the implementation also difficult.

(b) It is difficult to degrade all heavy metals and inorganic pollutants.

(c) Microbes do not degrade the pollutants completely. Sometimes, the by-product formed as a result of these reactions could be more toxic than the original pollutant.

(d) Adequate microbial population must be available for degrading the pollutants.

(v) Alternative materials : The nature of the waste material is one of the major criteria that has to be consider while planning waste handling and management. Some materials like plastic, fibre is very difficult to degrade. If we are able to find alternatives to such materials, then the waste management process becomes easier.

(a) In varied shapes and sizes, polythene bags are the biggest contributors of plastic waste. Polythene bags can be replaced by cloth or jute bags, which are reusable. Despite plastic ban in many states, these polythene bags are still in use. Paper bags are also recyclable.

(b) In occasions, disposable plates, cups and bowls are commonly used. This practice can be stopped and steel or ceramic plates should be used, which are re-usable.

(c) Usage of various recycled products like recycled fabric, tissue paper, doormats, etc. should be encouraged.

SUMMARY

- Waste is any substance which is discarded after its use.
- It can be classified under two broad areas : Biodegradable and Non-biodegradable waste.
- Waste can be also categorised based on their state *i.e.* , solid waste (garbage, electronic waste, etc.), liquid waste (sanitary waste, effluents, etc.) and gaseous waste (hazardous gases like NO_x, SO_x, CFC, etc. released from industries, vehicles, etc.).
- Each type of waste should be handled and disposed in an appropriate manner.
- Waste management or waste disposal includes the activities and actions required to manage waste from its inception to its final disposal. The activities include collection of waste, transport, treatment and disposal.
- A waste treatment process which includes the combustion of waste for recovering the energy is called as incineration.
- The 3R method (Reduce, Re-use and Recycle) is one of the most efficient method to prevent waste generation.
- Composting is a way of harnessing the natural process of decomposition to speed up the decay of waste.
- Vermicompost involves composting a mixture of decomposing food waste, bedding materials and vermicast.
- Bioremediation is a process used to treat contaminated media, including water, soil and subsurface material, by altering environmental conditions to stimulate growth of microorganisms and degrade the target pollutants.

EXERCISE

A. Define each of these terms :

1. Reuse
2. Reduce
3. Recycle
4. Vermiculture
5. Composting

B. Answer in brief :

1. Write any two benefits of incinerators.
2. Enlist any two drawbacks of incinerators.
3. Mention any two drawbacks and benefits of composting.
4. Why is it essential to maintain the moisture level in the vermicompost?
5. What is bioremediation?
6. What are the limitations of bio-remediation? (write any two points)
7. Name the process used in bio-remediation for converting waste material into less harmful substances.

C. Answer each of these in detail :

1. Explain the types of biodegradable wastes with examples.
2. Describe the types of landfills.
3. What is vermicompost? Describe the conditions required for maintenance and operation of vermincomposting.
4. Biotechnology finds significant application in waste management.Justify the statement.
5. Elaborate alternative ways of waste management.

D. Previous Years Board Questions :

1. Distinguish between biodegradable and non-biodegradable waste.
2. What are sanitary landfills? Explain how they can be made secure.
3. How are biodegradable wastes useful?
4. What is waste? Explain in detail three methods of waste disposal.
5. Name the three R's and explain any one.

WORKSHEET

(A) Complete the analogy :

1. Gypsum: Construction landfill ; Brick: ______.
2. Sewerage: Municipal waste; Fodder: _________.
3. Garbage burial: Landfill ; Garbage burning: _________.

(B) Justify the following statements :

1. Landfills cause a ground water pollution.
2. Incineration cause global warming.
3. Climatic condition affect composting period.
4. Composting improves soil profile.

(C) Read the following excerpt and answer the questions that follow. (open-ended questions) :

1. Pranav set-up a vermicompost plant to produce organic fertilizer. He observed that some worms died due to the dryness in the soil.
   (a) What should be the ideal moisture condition for vermicomposting?
   (b) Name the species of worms used for vermicomposting.
2. Sridhar is planning a party at his residence. Suggest a few tips to handle and manage the waste that could be generated at the party.

(D) Activities :

1. Research and prepare a report on the fermentation, redox reaction and denitrification reactions for waste management.

9 ENVIRONMENT AND DEVELOPMENT

1.0 INTRODUCTION

We depend on nature and its components (biotic as well as abiotic) in each and every step of our routine life. The tangible and intangible benefits that we reap from environment are inestimable. About ten thousand years ago when man changed his lifestyle from a nomad to an agriculturist, we made several changes to our environment that suited our lifestyle. We termed these changes as development or progress. In fact, the development or progress in the form of changes that we make are still going on. To make our lives comfortable, convenient, luxurious and lucrative we are continually making changes. But the changes that we have made to develop and progress are showing up negative impacts on the environment. Therefore, sustainable development has become the need of the hour.

1.1 GLOBAL ENVIRONMENTAL POLLUTION

Everybody is aiming at a better living. By better living, we mean good standards, comforts and facilities. Heavy development activities like construction, transportation, manufacturing, infrastructure building, etc. are being initiated and carried out. Execution of such activities requires acres of natural landscapes. These activities also accumulate enormous waste materials causing pollution of our precious natural resources like air, water and soil.

The effects and hazards of global environmental pollution are faced not only by a certain region, but the entire planet. Issues may have started numerous decades or hundreds of years' prior and are the consequence of added substance, interconnected occasions that are showed in a more unpredictable present-day problem. It might also be genuine that the issue was created at a moderately direct level of multifaceted nature. A magnificent case of this sort of global pollution is climate change which is mind boggling and requires the participation of all nations. Global climate change is linked with common changes in climate. A few people who will be resistant to change, can not foresee the results, demand their qualities are right and may have compelled ideological, social and political esteems and thoughts. This is all happening in a period of globalization in expanded inter– connectedness among nations in the regions of economy, exchange, culture, and politics.

Human activities or anthropogenic causes affect sour planet undesirably. A simple stone crusher adds a considerable amount of suspended particulate matter *i.e.* pollutant and noise into the atmosphere. Vehicles emit gases like oxides of nitrogen, sulphur dioxide, carbon dioxide, carbon monoxide and an intricate mixture of unburnt hydrocarbons and soot particles, which pollute the atmosphere. Domestic waste and agricultural run-off with pesticides and chemicals contaminate water bodies. Effluents from tanneries contain numerous destructive chemicals and transmit foul smell. These are cases which indicate how human activities contaminate nature. Contamination might be characterized as expansion of unwanted material into nature because of human intervention. The substance which causes environmental pollution are called pollutants. A pollutant might be characterized as a physical, chemical or natural substance unexpectedly discharged into the earth that affects people and other living life forms directly or indirectly.

Developed Vs. Developing countries – Who is responsible?

Climate change and global warming is caused due to enormous discharge of greenhouse gases like CO_2, CH_4, CFCs and nitrous oxide from various sources. In 18th and 19th century new technologies were invented to meet the growing demands of basic commodities like food, clothing, medicines, etc. This led to the set-up of first industrial factory. This era also witnessed the significant exhaustion of resources, emission of pollutants and onset of climate change, global warming, acid rain and ozone layer depletion. In other words, developed countries are heavily industrialised as compared to developing nations and release more greenhouse gases per capita than developing countries. In addition, they also have high number of automobiles which keeps adding on the pollutant emissions. The climate change, pollution, ozone layer depletion and global warming have now become global environmental issue. Though these are the global issues, unsustained development and over exhaustion of resources by the developed nations are majorly responsible for the present environmental scenario. The graph shows cumulated carbon dioxide emissions done by 10 nations. The emission quantity of USA which is one of the developed country and other developing countries are clearly depicted. However, reducing the impacts and taking measures to prevent environmental problems is the need of the hour and both developed countries as well as the developing countries should join hands to take steps towards reducing the same. All the nations should review and reconstruct their development plans and policies. A uniform capping on emissions cannot

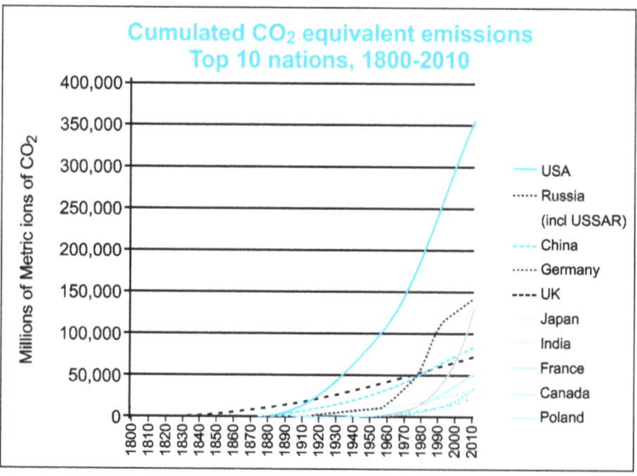

be done on all the countries. The development needs, the history of per capita emission of the nation, its geographic features, population, impact on its and on the world economy should be considered before levying controls on emissions. In the year 1992, United Nations Framework Convention on Climate Change (UNFCCC) formulated an international treaty called Kyoto Protocol. It is an international agreement that aims to reduce carbon dioxide emissions and the presence of greenhouse gases. As developed countries have already done more emissions compared to the developing countries or underdeveloped countries, the capping is more for the developed nations. The purpose of the Kyoto Protocol is to stabilize human-generated emissions at a level that will not inflict further harm on the atmosphere. The countries have to keep a check on emissions through carbon footprints. However, all countries have not accepted this treaty. Foot printing is accounting the amount of carbon dioxide released into the atmosphere as a result of the activities of a particular individual, organisation, or community. However, the nations which fail to control over the emissions are liable for the penalty. Each country is bearer of unique strengths, weaknesses, geographic features and climatic conditions. Developed nations are advanced in technology while underdeveloped and developing nations may have good reserves of natural resources. Countries have to engage with other countries to attain common welfare goals such as eradication of social evils, poverty and environmental degradation. The international organisations like United Nations (its various branches like UNFCCC, UNESCO, UNICEF, etc.), WWF, IUCN, WHO, etc. are working towards bringing more and more nations together.

? Intext Questions

1. What is per-capita emission?
2. What is Kyoto protocol?

1.2 ECONOMIC DEVELOPMENT AND ENVIRONMENTAL DEGRADATION

Economic growth drives the environmental degradation as most of the developmental activities happen at the cost of nature.

Economic development can disturb the quality of our environment through a wide range of human activity, composition and the effect of income on the demand and supply of the pollution reduction effort. The larger the range of economic activity, larger is the level of environmental degradation. It is because increased level of economic activity increases the usage of natural resources, ultimately resulting in more waste.

The primary sector does not cause much pollution when compared to secondary and tertiary sectors. However, the primary sector like agriculture and service depletes the available natural resources as it is resource-intensive sector. The secondary and tertiary sectors like oil refining, food processing, manufacturing, etc., tend to cause more pollution as they are pollution-intensive sectors. Since the structure of the economy changes, some portion of the impact of income per capita (person) reflects the impacts of the changing piece of output.

The impact can have a positive or negative effect on the environment since it quantifies the advancement of the economy towards a pretty much suitable beneficial structure. The specialized impact is the positive environmental outcomes of increments in wage that call for cleaner generation strategies. Higher salaries empower higher open consumption on environmental infrastructure and also environmental controls that drive private part use on reduction advancements.

Trade can very well influence the environmental degradation through wide range of developmental activities. Initially, it might look like a raise in economy and related activities but it actually consumes natural resource and create pollution.

Sulphur dioxide, carbon monoxide or nitrogen oxides are the prominent pollutants resulted from emissions through developmental activities.

Theoretically, it may be debated that the economy or our income increases with increase in the demand for environmental quality. Economic growth is indeed associated with increase in the consumption pattern, waste generation and carbon emissions. The sensitivity towards environment increases when people become rich or they meet their living standards.

Once their basic needs are met, they are ready to bear the cost of environmental deterioration or even pay to maintain the environmental quality.

One of the best difficulties threatening all nations has been the impacts or outcomes of worldwide environmental degradation. The economic literature on the effect of worldwide environmental degradation can be parted into two groups: climate change and other environmental indicators. We must concentrate more on climate change. This concentration might somewhat be clarified by the way that climate change will possibly undermine every one of the endeavours at environmental protection and may weaken human welfare. Environmental degradation may affect economic development through a few channels like migration, economic growth, well being, clashes and agriculture.

Fascinating Fact

More than 1 billion people worldwide don't have access to safe drinking water.

Environmental degradation in India

The real reasons for the environmental degradation are present day urbanisation, industrialization, population explosion, deforestation and so on. Environmental pollution refers to the degradation of value and amount of natural resources. Various types of the human activities are the principle reasons of environmental degradation. These have prompted environmental changes that have turned out to be destructive to every living being. The smoke radiated by the vehicles is toxic and also increases the amount of toxicity in air. The waste items, smoke emitted by vehicles and industries are the primary driver of pollution. Unplanned and unsustainable urbanization and industrialization have caused water, air and sound pollution. Urbanization and industrialization help to build pollution of water. Respectively, the smoke radiated by vehicles and industries like Chlorofluorocarbon, nitrogen oxide, carbon monoxide and other dust particles pollute air.

1.3 INTERNATIONAL TRADE

History is loaded with cases of how globalization has influenced environmental results. Human migration has significantly influenced the indigenous habitat. Much early trade was product based–fish, horticulture, timber and other crude materials. Further, we managed to cross the boundaries of the countries and continents for our businesses. International trade is the exchange of capital, goods, and services across international borders or territories. Exporting and importing materials across nations increased the environmental exploitation to the greater level. International trade policies should incorporate and reflect upon sustainable development goals (SDGs). Unfortunately, these goals were not taken care of while the onset of international trade. This led to various environmental problems and imbalances. The effect of international trade on the environment are listed as follows :

Fascinating Fact

1. The first multinational corporation was established in 1602 as the Dutch East India Company.

(i) Over cultivation : In order to meet the consumer demands, nations cultivate more crops, sometimes more than the land or soil capacity. To increase the soil productivity, fertilizers, pesticides, artificial hormones, etc. will be brought into use. Such practices lead to soil degradation, erosion and disturbed soil ecosystem.

(ii) Selected cultivation : Cultivators will be more focussed on growing the crops that are economically significant. Such practices impact our biodiversity, ecosystem and moreover we also give less chance to natural selection and evolution.

(ii) Over-exploitation : Over-exploitation of resources is one of the major bad face of international trade. Over-harvesting plant resources, animal resources, fuel, minerals, etc. is major threat to the environment and its components. Various major environmental problems like global warming, deforestation, pollution, man-made disasters, etc. are the effects of over-exploiting the resources.

However, formulation and follow up of robust and fair-trade policies can control environmental degradation to a great extent. International trade has brought about positive changes in many nations. Exposure to international market and consumer, availability of variety of goods to the consumers, exchange of knowledge on latest technology between the nations, international cooperation and better standards of living are some of the advantages of international trade. But, unfortunately many unfair trade practices are being witnessed. Unfair trade practice refers to the use of various deceptive, fake or unethical methods to obtain business. Unfair trade practices include misrepresentation, false advertising or representation of goods or service, false free prize or gift offers, deceptive pricing and non-compliance with manufacturing standards. Such acts are considered unlawful by Consumer Protection Law. Debt trap is also an important factor that determines the economic development of the nation. A debt trap is a situation in which a borrower is led into a cycle of re-borrowing, or rolling over, their loan payments because they are unable to afford the scheduled payments on the principal of a loan. The lender uses strategies like changing payments, high interest rates and high penalties for late payment of the instalments. These debts providing schemes are advantageous favour of the lender. The nations who get trapped in such schemes find it extremely difficult to repay the loan taken. As a result, the economic development and progress of that country gets hampered.

? Intext Questions

1. What is globalisation?
2. How does trade influence our economy?
3. What kind of products are traded from India?
4. Which organisation works and regulates International Trade?

1.4 ROLE OF MULTINATIONAL CORPORATIONS

Multinational Corporations (MNC) have an existence both in their nation of origin and in another nation. Since the destinations of such organisations can influence those in various nations, managers ought to be mindful so as to set applicable targets that will profit every one of the nations where the corporations have presence.

Some objectives of MNCs are as follows :

(i) Specific goal that the MNCs needs to reach and it must be something that managers can quantify.

(ii) To increase the profits with good customer service.

(iii) To grow at a definite rate, reaching a detailed sale, devising original products and acting socially dependable.

The MNCs today revolutionarily affect the international economic framework. Today they constitute an intense power on the economy. In the field of international trade and finances, the multinational firms have massive power. In mid-seventies the MNCs represented around one-eighth of all international trade. From the idea of their development it might be assumed that in the mid-eighties their offer will ascend to one-fourth. Among the developing nations just India has an annual income more than General Motors, which is the greatest multinational company. Generally, the yearly salary of least developed nations is considerably less than that of the MNCs. By mid-eighties, around 300 vast MNCs will come to control 75 percent of the world's manufacturing possessions. The significance of multinational corporations is not restricted to creation, as they are additionally huge members in international trade. It has been evaluated that trade inside MNCs, called intra-firm trade, represents around one-third of aggregate world trade. In the event that we add to this figure the trade that happens amongst MNCs and other unaffiliated firms, at that point MNCs are associated with around 66% of world trade.

1.5 BHOPAL GAS TRAGEDY

The Bhopal Gas tragedy is the worst environmental disaster in India. It happened at Bhopal on December 3, 1984.

The Union Carbide factory is situated in Bhopal, Madhya Pradesh. The game changing episode occurred because of the spillage of deadly gas called methyl isocyanate (MIC) gas from three stockpiling tanks of Union Carbide factory, a Multinational Corporation. MIC is an intermediate used for producing pesticides. Methyl isocyanate (MIC) is created by mix of phosgene, a lethal gas used during First World War with methyl amine. In the accident, about 36 tons of toxic MIC gas was discharged into the atmosphere. The gas causes burning sensation in the eyes, breathing problem and chest pain. Also, cyanide in the body turns lethal and leads to death.

Bhopal gas disaster caused the single greatest air pollution catastrophe, as indicated by official sources, with 2500 death cases. Some non-governmental sources put the figure considerably higher. As indicated by the figure released by the government, around 17,000 individuals have been rendered permanently weakened and another 30,000 partially disabled. The individuals who have suffered minor disabilities are around 1,50,000.

The Bhopal gas disaster polluted drinking water, soils, tank and lake water and also affected foetus, new-born babies, pregnant ladies, young and old people. It also killed numerous animals and countless micro-organisms.

This disaster is a burning case of one of the deadliest tragedy caused by human carelessness. A few evidences focus to basic safety provisions inside the plant carelessness of the authorities. They are as follows :

(i) The plant has two key safety procedures.

(a) Scrubbers that nullify the gas with caustic soda.

(b) Flare tower that burns off the gas.

(ii) Unfortunately, both of them did not work on that day.

(iii) The refrigeration units that stored MIC gas were not working for quite a few months.

(iv) The water jet failed to stretch to 120 feet load from where MIC gas leaked.

(v) The poisonous gas was in the tanks for around two months and that by itself was a violation.

(vi) Public siren was switched on an hour after the gas leakage.

(vii) Most importantly, the plant was situated in thickly populated area of old Bhopal.

Intext Question

1. Find out the other poisonous gases used in the chemical industries.

SUMMARY

- Global environmental problems include various environmental issues like pollution, global warming, ozone layer depletion, resource depletion, etc. which affect the entire planet.
- International trade policies should incorporate and reflect upon sustainable development goals (SDGs). However, these goals were ignored for a long duration which has invoked various environmental and social problems.
- Foot printing is accounting the amount of carbon dioxide released into the atmosphere as a result of the activities of a particular individual, organisation or community.
- The international organisations like United Nations (its various branches like UNFCCC, UNESCO, UNICEF, etc.), WWF, IUCN, WHO, etc. are working towards bringing more and more nations together.
- Economic growth drives the environmental degradation as most of the developmental activities happen at the cost of nature.
- International trade is the exchange of capital, goods, and services across international borders or territories.
- International trade policies should incorporate and reflect upon sustainable development goals (SDGs).
- There have been many unfair trade practices in the international trade. Unfair trade practice refers to the use of various deceptive, fake or unethical methods to obtain business.
- A *debt trap* is a situation in which a borrower is led into a cycle of re-borrowing, or rolling over, their loan payments because they are unable to afford the scheduled payments on the principal of a loan.
- Bhopal gas disaster caused the single greatest air pollution disaster, with approximately 2500 death cases.

A. Define each of these terms :

1. Pollution

2. Debt trap

3. MNCs

B. Answer the following in brief :

1. What is meant by urbanization? State the main effects of urbanization on environment.

2. In which year did Bhopal gas tragedy occur?
3. Who is responsible for environmental degradation? Discuss.
4. Discuss the Bhopal gas tragedy event?
5. How the activities of MNCs can be regulated?

C. Answer the following in detail :

1. Environment degradation is caused by developing countries. Give reason to support this statement.
2. How international trade is linked to environmental degradation? Discuss with suitable examples.
3. Discuss the contribution of MNCs to the development and debatable contribution to the environment.

D. Previous Years Board questions :

1. How can private enterprise contribute towards city improvement?
2. Define a multinational corporation.Give the primary objective of an MNC.
3. Suggest two strategies adopted by developing countries like India to control population.
4. Mention any two ways to reduce air pollution from domestic sources.
5. State two factors responsible for air pollution from automobiles.
6. Define global environment health.
7. What are the two unfair trade practices of the developed countries?
8. What is smog? State any one ill effect of it.
9. How has slowing down of economic growth created hardship for the urban poor?
10. List any two benefits of an MNC that influences the growth of developing nations.
11. State two ways in which the objectives of economic development can be achieved. Explain three of its effects that lead to environmental degradation.
12. Explain how you can plan environment of urban areas?
13. Discuss any five ways by which multinational companies cause environmental degradation in developing countries?
14. "Environmental resources are put under great stress in order to achieve the objectives of economic development." Explain.
15. Discuss any five ways of reducing air pollution caused by industries.
16. How can mass public transport with high capacity and low pollution been encouraged?

WORKSHEET

(A) Complete the Analogy :

1. The trade within the MNC is called ______trade.
2. The _________ is the method of accounting the amount of carbon dioxide released into the atmosphere as a result of the human activities.
3. The full form of UNICEF is _______.
4. In the year 1992, UNFCCC formulated an international treaty called ________.

(B) How does international trade stimulate each of these consequences :

1. Over-exploitation.
2. Over-cultivation.
3. Selected cultivation.
4. Global Environment Pollution.

(C) Read the following excerpts and answer the questions that follow. (open-ended questions) :

1. Few countries like USA, Taiwan, etc. did not sign the Kyoto Protocol.
   (a) List the probable reasons as to why these countries did not sign the Kyoto Protocol.
2. Countries have to engage with other countries to attain common welfare goals such as eradication of social evils, poverty and environmental degradation. Various international organisations are working towards bringing more and more nations together.
   (a) How does engagement of nations help in attaining welfare goals?

(D) Activities :

1. Research and prepare a report on the international trade policies that aims at sustainable development.

10 TOWARDS A SUSTAINABLE FUTURE

1.0 INTRODUCTION

Human development is often gauzed in terms of economic development or progress in technology. The nations are classified as developed, developing and under-developed based on economic and technological status. The developed nations have exploited a huge amount of natural resources in the process of achieving the current economic and technological status. As the development progressed rich countries got even richer while poor nations did not show much progress. An imbalance was evident. This form of development hampered environment and nature. However, by the 1970, the concerns regarding environmental conditions started getting considered. Environmental issues like pollution, global warming, ozone hole, resource exhaustion, loss of biodiversity pulled attention of environmentalists of all countries. The need for sustainable development was apparent.

1.1 GLOBAL INTERDEPENDENCE

The concepts and opinions involved in environmental protection and economics are often seen as contradictory. Rapid economic growth combined with a rapid population growth has placed great stress on the environment. Therefore, one of the great challenges of modern economics is to protect the environment. Un-sustained methods of achieving economic progress has adversely impacted environment. Pollution, global warming, ozone hole, resource exhaustion, loss of biodiversity are all effects of economic development. Therefore, it is important to base our economic development in such a way that availability of resources to the future generation is also considered. Such is the effect of economy on environment. However, environment also affects economy in following ways :

(i) Damage to the environment will threaten future living standards.

(ii) Pollution causes health problems and can damage the productivity of land and seas.

(iii) Volatile weather patterns could cause significant economic loss.

Fascinating Fact

America uses about 15 times more energy per person than the typical developing country.

Global Environmental Health

Global Environmental Health may be defined as research, education, training and research translation directed at health problems that are related to environmental exposures and excel national boundaries, with a goal of improving health for all people by reducing the environmental exposures that lead to preventable–disease, disabilities and deaths. Economic status is not the alone parameter to measure nation's development. Progress in environment management, equality, etc. is all criteria of development. Developed nations have not only exploited their resources, but also have used resources of developing and underdeveloped nations. The disparity in lifestyles between the rich and poor is unpleasant. Unsustainable development strategies have worsened these situations and widened the gap between the poor and the rich. Past experiences have proved that equity and harmony cannot be achieved without sound economic and environmental policies and involvement of all nations. Inequality is usually associated to an unequal distribution of resources and therefore, it is related to the gap between the rich and the poor. It also relates to an unequal access to opportunities or benefits from economic activity. Economic and social inequality can be mitigated by implementing these measures :

(i) Pro-poor fiscal policy

In informal markets, financial incentives for poorer entrepreneurs can encourage them to enter the formal sector. Some benefits from tax can be given considering status and profits.

(ii) Targeting of social programmes

Geographic targeting and survey data can be used to estimate poverty level of people. Participatory targeting can be done where people from the community identify and validate the selection of beneficiaries.

(iii) Participatory decision making

This strategy focuses on increasing the voice of the poor. Poor people often face an inequality of participation in policy making. Designing participatory methodologies to actually include their perspective in public policy can help reduce the gaps of power to decide over policies, which affect them and their communities.

(iv) Revision of laws and regulation that fosters inequality

This strategy can help to identify discriminatory laws or laws that generate inequalities among people or regions. The laws that do not recognize domestic labour as productive; or social security systems that do not provide universal access should be amended.

(v) Creating awareness and access to education

Economically underprivileged people, most of the times are not aware about current issues and advancements. As a result, they find it difficult to cope with fasting progressing world. Exposure and access to new technologies will help them to be updated with current trends. Awareness programmes related to their occupation and money saving schemes should be conducted, so their economic conditions are stabilised.

(vi) Corporate Social Responsibility

Corporate Social Responsibility (CSR) is a concept whereby organisations consider the interests of society by taking responsibility for the impact of their activities on customers, suppliers, employees, shareholders, communi-ties and the environment in all aspects of their operations. Companies are today obliged to certain responsibilities toward society and unprivileged class of people. The companies in collaboration with government and NGOs put their efforts to uplift the unprivileged people.

? Intext Questions

1. "The nations are classified as developed and under-developed based on economic and technological status", such a viewpoint has to be changed. Why ?
2. How does participatory decision making eliminate inequality?

1.2 INTERNATIONAL COOPERATION

Many global organisations like UN in association with its member states try to face common challenges (related to environment, inequality, poverty, etc.), manage shared responsibilities and frame action plan to facilitate enduring peaceful, inclusive and sustainably developing world.

(i) The Montreal Protocol

The Montreal Protocol on Substances that deplete the ozone layer is an international treaty designed to protect the ozone layer by banning the production and use of numerous substances that are responsible for ozone depletion. In 1973, the scientists were studying the effects of CFCs on atmosphere. They found that CFCs were stable till they reached the stratosphere. In the stratosphere, CFCs broke and decomposed to release radicals. The radicals thus released degrade the ozone layer. This treaty was brought in practice in 1990. Due to its widespread adoption, the Montreal protocol has been one of the most successful international treaties.

(ii) The Global Environment Facility (GEF)

The GEF was established in 1992 which aims at combating environmental issues like loss of biodiversity, climate change, pollution, international waters, land degradation, ozone depletion and forest management. It associates with several international institutions, civil society organizations and the private sector to fulfil the objectives. GEF was initiated in the Rio Summit. It collates the participation of 183 countries along with partnerships of private sectors, international institutions, multinational companies to formulate solutions for environmental problems and sustainability issues. GEF also operates independently to fund many organisations which are involved in initiatives like conservation of biodiversity, protection of forest, sustainable development, etc.

(iii) The Earth Summit

It is the Conference on Environment and Development held by the UN. The Earth Summit is also known as the Rio-de-Janerio Earth Summit or United Nations Conference on Environment and Development. Prior to the Earth Summit, the member states took initiatives internationally to solve environmental issues. However, after the cold war the tension between the countries led to many disputes and disagreement with each other. Such a discrepancy affected the functions carried out by the member states. Therefore, the Earth Summit was created. In this conference the leaders of the countries of the United Nations discussed ways of protecting the environment and preserving the earth's biodiversity.

(iv) International Conference on Population and Development (Cairo)

This conference was coordinated by UN in Cairo, Egypt in 1994. The issues like population explosion, immigration, infant mortality, birth control, family planning, the education of women and protection for women from unsafe abortion services were discussed.United Nation Population Fund (UNPF) was created as a result of this conference. The works of UNPF involves improvement of reproductive health, opposing child marriage, enlightening on safe child birth, etc.

(v) The Kyoto Treaty

Kyoto Protocol or treaty is an extension of United Nation Framework Conventions on Climate Change (UNFCCC). It is an international treaty that aims at reducing greenhouse gas emission. Reduction commit-ment varied from nation to nation. Each nation is required to set an agreed target of GHG emission. The GHG emission will be measured used carbon footprints. The percentage relaxation or the permitted amount of emission for developed countries was more than the developing or undeveloped nations. This variation was based on the fact that developed nations have already emitted huge amounts of GHGs and consumed huge amount of natural resources during the process of development. However, if countries violate the rules of the protocols or exceed the allotted relaxation of emission, then those nations would be eligible for penalty. There are around 192 participants for this protocol.

1.3 SUSTAINABLE DEVELOPMENT

In 1987, the World Commission on Environment and Development introduced the term Sustainable development in its report ***'Our Common Future'***. Sustainable development is development that meets the needs of the present without compromising the ability of future generations to meet their own needs. The agenda of sustainable development is holistic and universal.

The concept of sustainability links the concern for the carrying capacity of natural systems with the social, political and economic challenges faced by humanity. For sustainable development to be achieved, it is crucial to harmonise three core elements: economic growth, social inclusion and environmental protection. These elements are interconnected and are all crucial for the well–being of individuals and societies.

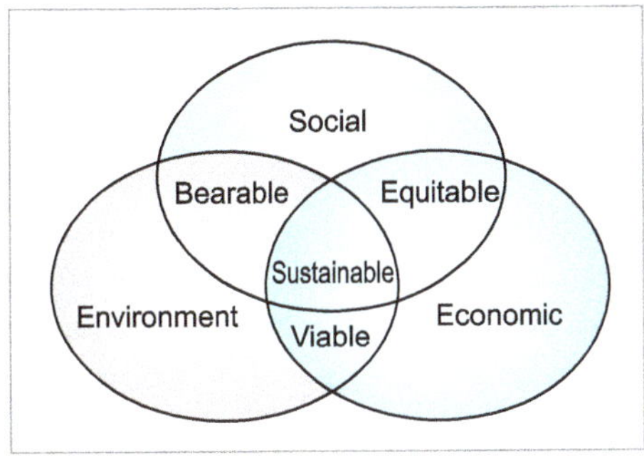

In September 2015, the United Nations General Assembly formally adopted a set of 17 Sustainable Development Goals (SDGs) that aims at transforming world by 2030. These goals focus at countering issues like :

(i) **People :** Ensuring healthy life, knowledge and inclusion of women and children.

(ii) **Planet :** Protecting our nature and ecosystem.

(iii) **Partnership :** Catalysing global solidarity.

(iv) **Justice :** Promoting safe and peaceful societies.

(v) **Prosperity :** Growing strong, inclusive and transforming economy.

(vi) **Equality :** Eradicating poverty and fight inequality.

Fascinating Fact

A 5-minute shower is equal to 20-35 gallons of water. Every time you open the refrigerator door, up to 30 percent of the cold air can escape.

Unfortunately, the practical application of sustainable development is unclear in many urban areas in developing countries. However, with current and emerging global challenges such as climate change, rapid urbanisation, environmental degradation, increasing poverty, food insecurity and financial crisis, a practical understanding of sustainable development is necessary and urgent especially in developing countries. Pure economic development needs to have some limits because the achievement of sustainable development requires the integration of not only its economic, but also its environmental and social components at all levels. If a society focuses only on the economic component, then it would be a society whose gross domestic product gets higher but at the same time also limits the chances of availability of resources for future generation. To check on unsustained policies of economic, laws and regulations should be implemented.

By 2050, it is estimated that the global population will become 9 billion. It is therefore necessary that developed as well as developing nations work towards sustainable development. If we fail to meet the challenges of sustainable development, the resources will fall inadequate for the growing population. Thus, sustainability should be a precondition for development. The developed countries are already coming up with various technologies to facilitate maximum resource extraction through minimal wastage. Similarly, developing nations should adopt green technologies. From the planning stage itself, the impact on environment and society should be considered. Criterion like employment opportunity, well-being, resource optimization, upliftment of the society, etc. should be incorporated at all the stages of starting and functioning of any project. The CSR (Corporate Social Responsibility) initiative taken up by many MNCs is a classic example of taking steps towards sustainability. Participation is an inevitable requirement of sustainability. Involvement of government, NGOs, MNCs, local communities, private sectors and international organisations is very important. More the involvement, better are the results. Participation of such bodies motivates all the citizens to give their contribution towards such noble cause.

1.4 ROLE OF NGOS IN FOSTERING SUSTAINABLE DEVELOPMENT

Non-governmental organisations (NGOs) are non-profit and international organisations independent of governments and international governmental organisations. NGOs have played a major role in pushing for sustainable development at the local, national and international level. NGOs have played important roles in bringing about a change in the system, laws and regulations. NGOs have many programs, functions and roles which assist community to become empowered and eventually attain sustainable development. Non-governmental organisations (NGOs) are engaged in multi-dimensional efforts that have been acknowledged globally in a number of development sectors, *i.e.*, education, health, poverty, environment etc. NGOs, through capacity building, develop community capacities such as ability, skill and knowledge of mobilizing resources, planning and evaluating community initiation and solving problems to gain the mastery over their lives. NGOs have better infrastructures and strategic paths to reach at grassroots level for empowering poor towards achieving sustainable development.NGOs have shown leadership in promoting sustainable community development. NGOs are good at reaching out to the poor and remote communities and mobilizing these populations. NGOs have focused attention on the social and environmental impacts of business activity.

Fascinating Fact

There are more than 1.2 million NGOs in India, out of which 53% are based in rural while 47% in urban areas.

1.5 SUSTAINABLE TECHNOLOGIES

(i) Use of satellites

Satellites are ideal for observing the global environment as they are capable of revealing and monitoring remote environments, hidden features, and even events that the human eye cannot detect. They provide reliable data 24 hours a day, seven days a week on the following atmospheric phenomena that are essential for weather forecasting. Satellites are ideal for monitoring climate change because they can monitor the concentration of greenhouse gases in the atmosphere, such as aerosols, water vapour, carbon monoxide, carbon-dioxide and methane. They also help to track the likely major impacts of climate change, such as global temperatures, weather patterns, the number and intensity of tropical cyclones, floods, droughts, sea level rise, changes in ocean currents, geographical shifts of ecosystems, vegetation health, melting of glaciers and polar ice, bleaching of coral reefs, wildfires, ocean acidification and changes in wildlife migratory patterns. Remote sensing satellites analyse images from observation satellites on a daily basis and scan them for possible changes. For example, when too much flora in one particular area starts disappearing, this can be an indication that illegal logging or deforestation is taking place. With remote sensing, habitat change can be seen as a result of human activities and suggest counter measures. The method provides the field of conservation with many new possibilities to precisely and quickly capture data and therefore to react much faster than before and to implement protective measures. The satellites have been monitoring ozone layer and providing valuable data to the scientists. With this information, scientists can better estimate the timing of the ozone layer recovery. Thematic Mapper data obtained from satellites are helpful in identifying and classifying the types of wastelands as sands, gullied land, salt affected areas and barren rocky area. Depending upon the nature of wasteland, suitable rehabilitation measures like plantations, afforestation can be proposed. Satellite imagery and aerial photography have proven to be important tools in support of mineral exploration projects. It helps in not only locating the minerals but also give information to do infrastructure planning, environmental impact studies, grassroots exploration and ground access studies. Remote sensing observations have been used to monitor drought and flood related variables from a climatologically viewpoint and also to assess and quantify drought impacts from an ecosystem perspective. Following are the advantages of remote sensing in comparison to the conventional methods :

(a) Satellite images are authentic and permanent records.

(b) It covers large area, making the study and research of those areas easier.

(c) Remote sensing is comparatively cheaper and less tedious method constructing map and land evaluation.

(d) It is the most convenient way to construct maps of inaccessible lands like Antarctica.

(e) It is easy to combine with other geographic coverages in the GIS.

(ii) Alternative technology

A sustainable society is the one that ensures the health and vitality of its citizens for present and future generations. Such societies are inhabited by people who are dedicated towards minimization of required inputs of energy, water, food, waste, output of heat, and pollution. Replacing better technologies and practices with the current ones is essential to ensure sustainable development. Opting for alternative technology is a good step towards building a sustainable society. Alternative technology refers to technologies that are more environment friendly than the ones in current practice.

(a) Using alternative energy source : Renewable energy sources, such as wind turbines, solar panels, or bio-gas created from sewage can be used.

(b) Sustainable transportation : Sus-tainable transport refers to the transport system that is sustainable in the senses of social, environmental and climate impacts. Vehicles contribute to lot of Green house gases (GHGs). The environmental impacts of transport can be reduced by reducing the weight of vehicles, sustainable styles of driving, reducing the friction of tires, encouraging electric and hybrid vehicles, improving the walking and cycling environment in cities and by enhancing the role of public transport.

(c) Sustainable building design : Sustainable architecture encompasses all phases of building including the planning, building, and restructuring. Construction of Zero Energy Buildings, installation of green roofs is some of the sustainable architecture strategies.

(d) Participation and engagement : Environment and social equity which are the two main elements of sustainable development can be achieved without the participation of citizens. Awareness and sense of responsibility towards issues like eradicating pollution, social evils, population explosion, over use of resources is crucial.

(iii) Role of biotechnology in eradicating global food scarcity

Biotechnology is the use of living systems and organisms to develop or make products, that uses biological systems, living organisms or derivatives to make or modify products or processes for specific use. Modern food biotechnology increases the speed and precision with which scientists can improve food traits and production practices. Biotechnological tools have greatly contributed to the production and supply of improved quality seed and planting material to farmers worldwide.

Biotechnology is employed to :

(a) Speed-up the multiplication process for vegetatively propagated crops.

(b) Detect diseases transmitted by seed or planting material.

(c) Eradicate diseases transmitted by planting material.

(d) Protect seed with biological control agents.

(e) Test varietal identity and purity.

The contribution given by Genetically Modified Crops in the field of agriculture and food production is remarkable. Genetically modified crops (biotech crops) whose DNA has been modified with genetic engineering techniques. The objective of genetically modified crops is to introduce new trait in them which do not occur naturally. Resistance to pests, diseases, stressful environmental conditions, chemical fertilizers and insecticides are some of the traits that are not innate in plants. The nutritive value, maturation time can be also enhanced using biotechnology.

A classic example in this context is production of golden rice through genetic engineering. Golden rice is a strain of rice in which beta-carotene, a precursor of vitamin A was incorporated. As a result, normal rice which is only rich in carbohydrates, also produced Vitamin A and it is the staple food of people of many countries, hence this process served the purpose of fortification also.

The unsustainable plans of development may yield short term economic benefits, but it does not guaranty healthy and safe future for coming generations. This implies that we need to better understand the future limits to growth and use this understanding to reconfigure growth in a way that is increasingly sustainable. The sustainable way of progressing is the only way which ensures holistic development.

SUMMARY

- Rapid economic growth combined with a rapid population growth has placed great stress on the environment.
- One of the great challenges of modern economics is to protect the environment.
- Unsustained methods of achieving economic progress has adversely impacted environment through pollution, global warming, ozone hole, resource exhaustion, loss of biodiversity, etc.
- Global Environmental Health focuses on health problems that are related to environmental exposures. It also aims at setting goals and taking actions to mitigate such health problems.
- Many international organisations are working on enduring peaceful, inclusive and sustainably developing world.

- Sustainable development is development that meets the needs of the present without compromising the ability of future generations to meet their own needs.
- Non-governmental organizations (NGOs) are non-profit and international organizations independent of governments and international governmental organizations. They have played a major role in pushing the sustainable development at the local, national and international level.
- Various sustainable technologies like using alternative source of energy, measures to reduce pollution; technologies to increase productivity from resources should be employed.

A. Define each of these terms :

1. Sustainable development
2. Globalization
3. NGOs
4. Biotechnology
5. Global environmental health

B. Answer the following in brief :

1. How does environment affect economy?
2. List out the main objectives of Sustainable Development Goals.
3. How are Genetically Modified Crops beneficial?
4. Why global environmental health is needed for the economic development of any country?
5. Differentiate between the aims of developing and developed countries towards the sustainable development?
6. What is meant by alternative technology. Give its three major advantages.

C. Answer the following in detail :

1. How can we mitigate economic and social inequality?
2. How do international cooperation hasten sustainability worldwide? Explain with reference to any three international cooperations.
3. How do NGOs catalyse sustainable development?
4. How does biotechnology help in better food production?
5. Write short notes on :
   (a) Kyoto Treaty
   (b) Montreal Protocol

D. Previous Years Board Questions :

1. Why is biotechnology used in agriculture?
2. Suggest two alternating technologies to create self-sustaining society.
3. What is Kyoto protocol? State its main objective.
4. Define sustainable development. Explain its major objectives.

WORKSHEET

(A) Fill in the Blanks :

1. The __________ was initiated in the Rio Summit.
2. The Kyoto Protocol is an extension of __________.
3. The concept of MNCs taking up responsibility of upliftment of society is called _________ .
4. The ___________ was created as a result of International Conference on Population and Development.

(B) How does following factors facilitate Sustainable future :

1. Pro-poo fiscal policy.
2. Creating awareness and access to education.
3. Zero energy buildings.
4. Participation and engagement
5. Advancement in biotechnology.

(C) Read the following excerpts and answer the questions that follow (open-ended questions) :

1. Observe the graph and answer the questions that follow :

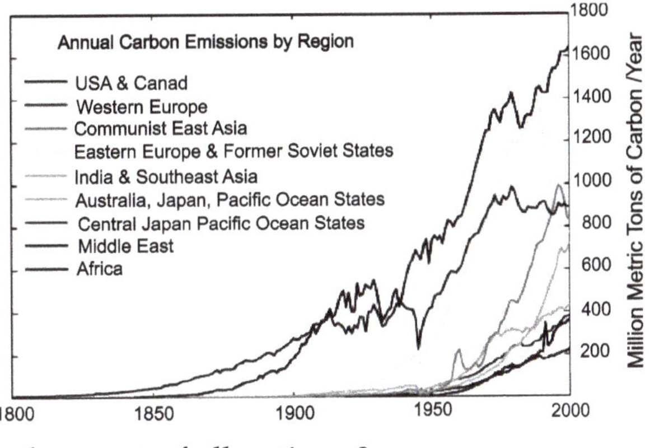

   (a) How would you justify the imbalance in the resource depletion among the nations ?

   (b) How would implementation of Kyoto protocol help in bringing about balanced and sustained development of all nations ?

2. Below given is the data collected by one of the leading business magazines. Observe the data given and answer the questions that follow :

The 2017 Sustainable Development Goals Inde					
Rank	**Country**	**Score**	**Rank**	**Country**	**Score**
1.	Sweden	85.6	7.	Austria	81.4
2.	Denmark	84.2	8.	Switzerland	81.2
3.	Finland	84	9.	Slovenia	80.5
5.	Czech Republic	81.9	116	India	58.1
6.	Germany	81.7	—	—	—

(a) Enlist the probable reasons as to why India ranks a low score in achieving sustainable development.

(b) What measures should be taken to ensure a sustainable future?

(D) Activities :

1. Visit an industry or a multi-national corporation in your locality. Find out about their CSR activities and make a report on the same. The report should include the information on planning and execution of the activities.
2. Divide your class into groups. Each group will take one sustainable development goal. Now discuss and make a poster depicting ways to attain the chosen sustainable development goal. With the help of your teachers, plan for an interactive seminar on the SDGs with the students for class 5 to 9 of your school. Use the posters that you have made in the seminar.

www.ingramcontent.com/pod-product-compliance
Ingram Content Group UK Ltd.
Pitfield, Milton Keynes, MK11 3LW, UK
UKHW050141280726
14058UKWH00006B/762

9 789389 937978